HEROES OF
CIVILIZATION

HEROES OF
CIVILIZATION

Revised Edition

by

JOSEPH COTTLER

and

HAYM JAFFE

BOSTON   Little, Brown and Company   TORONTO

LIBRARY OF CONGRESS CATALOG CARD NO. 69–10655

REVISED EDITION

*Published simultaneously in Canada
by Little, Brown & Company (Canada) Limited*

PRINTED IN THE UNITED STATES OF AMERICA

Everyone has his heroes. They are those people whom we admire so much that we would like to model ourselves after them. Choosing our heroes therefore is a serious matter. The authors of this book asked themselves these questions:

What sort of famous people do we admire?

Our heroes ought to be fighters, but fighters for what? On what battlefield? Against what enemy? And for whose benefit?

Well, we searched and we found our heroes. Here are some of them and their stories.

CONTENTS

BOOK I

Heroes of Exploration

BOOK II

Heroes of Pure Science

BOOK III

Heroes of Invention

BOOK IV

Heroes of Biology and Medicine

BOOK I

Heroes
of Exploration

Marco Polo

(c. 1254–1324)

A TRIP TO CATHAY

I

LIKE ALL BOYS of Venice, Marco used to go down to the port whenever a ship sailed in. Everyone crowded around while the sailors unloaded the cargo on the quay, piling up silks and carpets, woolens and furs, and huge lumps of metal. Standing apart from the rest, Marco would run his hand along the hulk of the ship. By what strange shores had it dropped anchor? What scented winds had filled its sails? When the others had gone up to the *piazza* to watch tumblers or listen to street singers, Marco stayed behind. Touching the beaten sides of the ship with his hand gave Marco a sense of faraway lands. It also gave him a sense of being near his father, who had left Venice when Marco was six.

"Father is away on business," his mother had said. Ever since then, the small boy used to go down to the port whenever a ship sailed in. He would sidle up to one of the ship's crew.

"Where have you come from?"

If the answer was Sicily or France or any other place

west of Italy, Marco did not follow with his second
question. But if the answer was Layas or Trebizond, he
would ask quickly: "Did you meet my father?" and he
would confide: "He is with my uncle Maffeo."

As time went by, the image of his father caused him
less pain. But the sense of the faraway grew stronger.
The sound of exotic place names made him restless.
Bagdad, Bokhara, Bosphorus. He wondered what sort
of people lived there, how they dressed and spoke and
how they prayed.

When Marco was fifteen his mother died. He was
cared for by his grandparents, and, still thinking of his
father, he asked them: "What lands lie behind Persia?"

His grandfather shrugged. "Who knows? We hear
about a land of people with only one foot, or with only
one eye in the middle of their forehead. These may be
fables. Perhaps there are no lands beyond Persia. The
earth seems to be shaped like a box, so that beyond the
borders of Persia there may be only the edge of the
world. But why bother your head about it? We live in
the greatest city. A child born in Venice is another nobleman added to the world. The best thing in life you
can hope for, dear Marco, is to become a merchant of
Venice like your father."

One day, the brightest in Marco's life, a ship sailed
into port and two strangers debarked. They were
dressed outlandishly. Seeing them, Marco felt his heart
pound. Their eyes met for an instant, and Nicolo Polo
caught his son in his arms. When they were a bit
calmer, father regaled son with stories of wild horsemen, of magicians, of deserts said to be inhabited by

evil spirits. But mostly he spoke of a marvelous country thousands of miles to the east where the sun rises.

"We in Venice," he said, "think of ourselves as the greatest nation on earth. But Maffeo and I have seen cities so splendid that in comparison with them Venice is a village."

Venetians laughed at such talk. Even Marco, so enchanted by the faraway, even he was incredulous. Could there be anything more magnificent than St. Mark's Cathedral? Venice was mistress of the seas and the very hub of trade in Europe. It was also the beating heart of Europe's culture.

"Well, you will see for yourself," said his father. "We shall return to China, and if you wish you may go with us."

If he wished! In November of the year 1271 the party started for the Orient, a region unknown to Europeans. Marco was seventeen years old.

Layas, Trebizond. The musical place names turned into gay cities, landscapes and people. The main road led from the Black Sea south to the Persian Gulf. All along the way Marco noted the lush Persian gardens and fertile plains. The party traveled on horseback at the rate of about twenty miles a day. Besides the Polos, there were two guides and two armed guards, for the road was treacherous and infested with bandits. Until they reached the gulf, however, the journey was as pleasant as a picnic. But when they left the city of Kerman and turned northeast, the way became hard. First, one hundred miles of desert. Then a climb of ten thousand feet, and they almost froze. Then a descent to sea level, where they almost suffocated with heat. As they proceeded, Marco noticed the changing features of the natives. They became squat and their faces bronzed and bony. The landscape, too, became emptier. Ominously, another range of mountains appeared in the east.

The party fell in with a caravan and for greater safety joined forces with it. This move was nearly fatal, for the caravan was attacked by a band of robbers. The Polos barely escaped behind the walls of a village. They might have been slain or sold for slaves.

The village was one of many Marco was to come across on the steppes of Asia: a few hundred human beings huddled together in the solitude of nature. They tended their livestock, grew corn and grapes, and spent their days anxious only about food, shelter and defense against enemies.

Marco was dismayed to hear his father and uncle consider turning back. If they did turn back, Marco feared they would never know what lay on the other side of the mountains. He was relieved when the men decided to risk the dangers ahead.

They were now riding along the border between Afghanistan and Persia and they came to the ancient city of Balkh. There they decided to rest awhile before beginning their climb to the Roof of the World, as the Pamirs were called. In the streets of the city Marco noted the mixture of races: swarthy Persians, men from beyond the Russian border with ruddy faces and blue eyes, slant-eyed Mongols, darkskinned men from India. Balkh had been the eastern outpost of the empire of Alexander the Great. Once many fine buildings had lined its streets. Now they were in ruins, laid waste by the Mongol general Genghis Khan. The Mongols had overrun and conquered China and indeed all of Asia. The grandson of Genghis ruled China, and it was to his court that the Polos were bound.

Crossing the Roof of the World was Marco's greatest physical ordeal. Partway up, the party came to the tableland of Badakhshan, where they found themselves in a grassy plain watered by sparkling streams. Occasionally they came upon camps of nomads who with their herds of cattle moved from pasture to pasture.

After resting for a season at Badakhshan the party continued the steep climb upward to what Marco thought must indeed be the top of the world. They came to a frozen lake, the source of the Oxus River. On all sides they were being watched by the wild denizens of the place, mountain sheep with enormous curly horns.

Now began the descent. They thought the worst over, and when they came to the city of Kashgar with its lovely gardens, they were sure of it. The pleasant illusion lasted until they reached Yarkand. Beyond this city the way was made hideous for them by frequent stretches of desert. Now and then they were able to refresh themselves at a meager oasis. But for a thousand miles they had to push through sand, only at the end of it to arrive at the Gobi Desert, the haunt — so Marco was told — of demons.

"If you should fall behind the rest of us," warned one of the guides, "you will hear spirits talking. They will call out 'Marco, Marco,' in the tones of one of us. That could lead you astray. Or you may hear the tramp of a great caravan and follow its ghostly sound. If you do, that will be the end of you."

Marco took care not to fall behind.

Once the Gobi Desert was crossed the party met with no further serious hardships. The features of the natives were now mostly of a yellowish tinge. Their eyes were slanted, their cheekbones prominent, and they had straight black hair. One morning as the party neared the Hwang Ho (Yellow River), they were met by a troop of cavalry sent by the Khan to escort them to his summer palace at Shangtu. It was summer in the year 1274.

Three and a half years had passed since the Polos left Venice. On foot or on horse they had traversed the vast steppes of Asia, climbed the snow-covered heights of the Pamirs, slogged through the sands of the Gobi Desert. It was almost incredible that they should at last have safely arrived in a world of whose existence the people of Venice knew nothing. Marco was now in his twentieth year. Around him were people whose faces were not like those with whom he had been familiar. Their speech was utterly strange. He might have been frightened, but the people kept smiling and bowing, and he found himself bowing and smiling in turn.

II

"And the young man, who is he?" Kublai Khan, the emperor, had brilliant black eyes and an ivory skin. The ends of his mustache were turned down outlining a square jaw. He gave the Europeans audience in the

throne room of the summer palace. Columns of orna-
mented marble supported the ceiling. The walls were
adorned with gilt dragons and heraldic beasts and
birds.

"Sire," said Nicolo Polo, "he is your servant and my
son."

"He is welcome. He pleases me."

At a glance the emperor saw in the European youth
the kind of intelligence and courage needed by his government. For his part Marco saw in opulent China his
golden opportunity. So began years of friendship between the young Italian and the Mongol Emperor.
Marco came to admire Kublai Khan for his sense of
justice and charity. He learned that the Khan took care
that his subjects never suffered poverty. Whenever
there was a poor harvest or a pestilence among cattle he
did not take his taxes. More than that, he sent grain
and cattle from his own stores to relieve the suffering.
He was tolerant of all forms of religious worship and
himself observed the holidays of every religion.

Marco knew that his career depended on mastering
the Mongol tongue as well as other languages of China.
He set to work at once studying them.

In the fall of the year the court moved to Peking, and
the Khan invited the Europeans to stay at his palace.
The city of Peking was enclosed by a wall thirty feet
high. At each corner of the wall there was a fort. Within
the city the Khan's palace was set in a spacious park
likewise walled around and fortified. The city was
beautiful. It had none of the narrow crooked streets of
European cities. In Peking the streets were broad and

straight. Every family had its own house and garden.
What an ingenious people, thought Marco. At home
people would accuse him of lying when he told them
that the Chinese used money made of paper. They
might believe his story of stoves and bath houses. But
what about rocks that burned (coal) and a kind of
paper (asbestos) which didn't burn and which they
used to fireproof buildings.

Three years after his arrival Marco was appointed
the emperor's special envoy. His duties were to tour the
realm and survey the condition of the people. As the
emperor's representative he was invested with all the
pomp of power, and set out on his tour of inspection
escorted by a retinue of servants and soldiers.

Notebook in hand, he journeyed south and then west,
by land and sea. In later times Kublai Khan said that
he learned more about his people from Marco's reports
than from those of any other envoy. For Marco made
notes not only of the industry of the people but of their
folkways, the splendor of their art and their forms of
religious worship. The extent of his travels was un-
equaled in his time. He visited the countries now called
Vietnam, Laos and Thailand. He visited the islands of
Java, Sumatra, Ceylon. He went to Tibet, to Burma,
and to India. In a ship so large that it required a crew
of three hundred (would the people at home believe
it?) he skirted the eastern shore of Africa and Arabia.
The peoples he visited ranged in color from white
Arabs through olive-skinned Malays to black-skinned
Indians. In level of culture they ranged from the primitive tribes of the Andaman Islands to the highly civilized people of Hangchow in China proper. Marco gave

account of their farms and vineyards, their production from delicate lace to iron tools. Their religious faiths had four names: Hinduism, which taught that the unseen world of the spirit was in all things and in all creatures; Buddhism, founded by Prince Gotama (called the Buddha, meaning Enlightened One), who taught that each of us was responsible for the suffering of his neighbor; Taoism (Tao means The Way), based on similar doctrine taught by the sage Lao-tse; and Confucianism, founded by the Chinese sage who taught: "What you do not want done to yourself, don't do to others."

The years flowed by and the elder Polos began to long for home. They had been away for eighteen years.

One day the old Khan called them to him. "You have been faithful to me," he said. "Be faithful still. The Khan of Persia wishes to marry one of our princesses. The voyage to his country is long and dangerous, and I fear to trust my own men with the life of the dear girl. But you who are skillful navigators could be trusted to convey her safely down the China Sea, past Sumatra and across the Indian Ocean to Persia.

And so, after twenty-four years of absence, in the year 1295, the Polos came back at last to their native Venice.

III

"Tell us, Marco. Tell us of the country where the men are fifty feet tall."

"Those I have not seen. Now in the islands of the

Indian Ocean there are indeed apes so large that they seem to be men!"

"What about pygmies? Are they really so small that they are nourished on the smell of apples?"

"Not that I know of."

"Did you ever meet with a jinn?"

"No, never."

"Is it true that in parts of China it is the custom for children to kill their parents?"

"Quite the opposite. In all parts of China it is the custom for children to revere their parents."

"Now that you've traveled all over the world don't you agree that Venice is the greatest and the best city?"

"I can't agree. In a very small way, though, Venice does resemble the city of Hangchow. Like Venice, Hangchow rests upon lagoons of water. But there the lagoons are spanned by twelve thousand bridges, all of them built of stone. Hangchow is fifteen times as large as Venice. The main street is two hundred feet wide and lined with houses, gardens, shops, palaces, temples. Along the canals are the warehouses of merchants in comparison with whom we, with all our great wealth, are like poor men. The sails that crowd into the city unload a hundred times more pepper, aloes, sandalwood, nutmeg, spikenard and ebony than in all the ports of Europe."

"Oh what a dreamer you are, Marco."

They didn't believe him. Nevertheless, he made a book of his travels. He put in writing what only he of all Europeans of his time had seen with his eyes. He wished his book to be an inspiration to later explorers. He hoped that it might help East and West know each other. By exchanging their different products both would be richer. By sharing ideas both would be wiser. And by knowing their differences they would find that they weren't so different after all.

Vasco da Gama

(c. 1460–1524)

INDIA AT LAST

I

IN THE AUDIENCE chamber of the King of Portugal, young Prince Henry was pacing to and fro.

"Patience, my son," counseled King John. "The prior will soon be here."

A servant entered announcing, "The Prior of the Hospitalers, Your Majesty."

"Let him come in," replied the king.

An elderly gentleman dressed in the robes of the Order of the Knights Hospitalers entered. With the king were his three sons. Cordially all greeted the prior, and questioned him anxiously about the secret journey he had just made. The prior smiled.

"What have you found" asked the impatient Prince Henry.

"Sire," the prior replied slowly, "I prefer not to speak of what I have found and seen until I have two sacks of sand . . ."

"Two sacks of sand!" the amazed prince exclaimed.

"Two sacks of sand," repeated the prior, "a reel of ribbon, and half a bushel of beans."

"Are you a wizard," laughed the king, "and are we to have some magic ceremony?"

The prior gravely bowed.

"I would not dare jest with Your Majesty," he solemnly replied, "but I would beg to repeat my request."

The princes of the realm laughed, too.

"Hear how he answers!" said King John, turning to his sons. "I sent him to spy out the town of Ceuta. When now I ask for an account of his journey, he replies by calling for sand and beans."

Nevertheless the good King John smilingly commanded that the prior's wish be fulfilled.

"Would not a little gravy make the beans more palatable?" jested the king, when these articles were carried in. "And the sand, should it not first be baked?"

The prior remained gravely silent.

"I would request that Your Majesty give me a room where I can spread these articles on the floor."

"Stranger and Stranger," muttered Prince Henry.

The sand, ribbon, and beans were accordingly placed in an adjoining chamber. Saying he would call them in a short while, the prior retired.

"The good prior must have been studying the Black Arts," ventured Prince Peter.

"Why does he make a mystery of this?" Prince Henry demanded. "We sent him to bring us an exact description of Ceuta town and its harbor. It seems to have affected his mind."

"The prior is a very wise and aged counselor," the king suggested. "Perhaps he knows a better way to describe Ceuta town than by words. Although I am just as curious as any of you, let us be patient."

While he was still speaking, the door opened, and the prior appeared. "Now, Your Majesty," he said, "the result of my labors can be seen. Your very eyes shall behold the town of Ceuta, and you can answer your own questions."

He stood respectfully aside, while the king and the three princes eagerly entered the room.

On the stone floor they saw molded in sand a large map of the Strait of Gibraltar. They could trace the southern coast of Spain with its mountains, and on the other side of the Strait the headland of Ceuta extending into the sea.

The beans were arranged in rows, like the streets of the city. A piece of ribbon showed the contour of the walls. The beach and landing places were indicated by sand. . . .

"An excellent way of describing a place. Your own eyes tell you about it," marveled the king. "With this plan, I think I could go about the city without getting lost."

While the others were admiring the map, Prince Henry was deep in thought. "If a town with its harbor can thus be shown," he mused, "why not a whole country? I think I can make a map of Portugal; indeed, one of all the world. I can do it."

Walking into the garden, he resolved, "I shall do it, but I must know more about the world. To the south of us is Africa with its mysteries, and to the east is magic India. What do I know for certain about these?" Prince Henry stopped to kick aside some gravel. "I have it!" he exclaimed. "I shall send men to explore Africa and bring me the truth about that continent, and ships —

whole fleets of them — to sail about Africa and perhaps reach India, the land of spice and silks. That is how I'll serve my country, Portugal, and the world."

II

Eighty-two years had passed. From a small country, Prince Henry's expeditions along the coast of Africa had made Portugal into a great empire.

Dom Manuel, King of Portugal, was sitting in the throne room of his palace. Around him were grouped his counselors. They were discussing explorations.

First Counselor: Columbus has failed.

Second Counselor: He found a new and surprising country.

First Counselor: But it is not India. What wealth can he get from this new land? In India, however, we have heard there are silks and precious stones and spices, and . . .

Second Counselor: But can we reach India? Where is it?

First Counselor: That is not the question. The question is *who* can reach India? The great Prince Henry the Navigator has shown us the way. Now who will follow? It took the great Marco Polo to lift the veil from China, and no less a man can reach India by sea.

Dom Manuel sat quietly thinking. As his counselor had so well put it, "Who can reach India?" Portugal boasted good mariners. But for this heroic and dangerous quest only a great one could serve. Who?

"Well," said one, "we have Diaz who went to the Stormy Cape."

"You know I have forbidden the term 'Stormy Cape,' " interrupted Dom Manuel. "We must not discourage our sailors. Say 'Cape of Good Hope.' "

"Well then, Diaz reached the Cape of Good Hope. That is sufficient proof of his great skill."

"But India is far beyond the Cape," broke in another. "Dom Manuel, . . ."

The king was not listening. During the discussion a young man had crossed the hall and was about to disappear through the spacious portal on the other side. He seemed a young man in his thirties, tall, with black hair, black beard, and striking, fierce eyes.

Dom Manuel was watching him intently. "Who is that?" the king asked.

"A gentleman of your court, sire," said the counselor, surprised.

"His name?"

"Oh, that is Vasco da Gama, Paulo's younger brother."

"He seems dashing. Is he as good a navigator as his brother?"

"He is very resolute and daring," said the counselor. "The da Gamas have all been great navigators. But Vasco is young."

"All the better," responded the king. "He may be the braver for his youth. Call him here."

The young man approached. Dom Manuel regarded him fixedly. "Vasco da Gama," said he slowly, "the man who will make neighbors of the great unknown people of the oriental lands of India and our peoples of the

West — that man, Vasco da Gama, will win everlasting glory."

The young man knelt down. "Sire," said he, trembling with joy, "I would give my life to be that man."

The king rose to his feet. "Arise, Commander," he pronounced. "And prepare your fleet."

That was how Vasco da Gama was chosen. Building his fleet of four ships and choosing his force of one hundred seventy men was a task of much love and little time. While he made these preparations, moreover, he carefully studied his maps and charts, and Ptolemy's geography. Then, having read thoroughly *The Book of Ser Marco Polo,* as Columbus had done, he felt ready to unfurl his sails.

On a summer day he weighed anchor. A great throng, in solemn parade, marched with him in the blazing sun along the beach of Belem — a beach of tears. Friends and relatives embraced and said their last farewells. Then da Gama and his comrades took leave of the weeping multitude and rowed out to their ships.

"They will never come back," a mother wailed. "The great Sea of Darkness will swallow them all."

Everyone knew that. Everyone knew that when the frail ships tossed between sea and sky, all the men would turn a strange color. Every child whispered tales of sea monsters and sirens that preyed on rash adventurers. There was the sea unicorn waiting, whose horn could pierce three ships at one blow. Vast and menacing were the dreadful phantoms of the sea. And even if da Gama escaped these haunting phantoms, there were yet the sheets of flame and boiling waters.

"They will never come back," mourned the watchers, as their eyes followed the dwindling sails. At the edge of the sea, the white specks slowly sank, trembled for a moment on the horizon, and vanished.

Silently the crowd turned homeward.

III

Onward sailed the little fleet; toward the flaming waters and fabled monsters perhaps. Day after day, week after week, stretched only the dreary wastes of sea and sky. Vasco da Gama sat in his lookout. His fearless eyes betrayed no shadow of the anxiety he felt.

He could not help but feel troubled. For months there had been no sign of the promised land. The men were becoming uneasy and a bit fearful.

"Perhaps we are following da Gama to our doom," some even thought.

Da Gama knew besides what his men did not, that they were nearing the dreaded Cape of Good Hope. There they might all be wrecked by the frightful storms that continually raged. If only they could round the Cape, they were safe. But come what might, da Gama determined never to turn back, even though he battled the storm to his death. Round the Cape or die!

They passed by a broad bay which was not on his chart. "Let its name be St. Helena Bay" said da Gama.

Winter was setting in and as the fleet approached the Cape the waters grew rougher. Da Gama's anxiety was intense as he girded himself for the struggle. He prayed that all his men might be in good health and high spirits, his ships trim and sturdy.

Suddenly, an unlooked-for misfortune visited them.

A disease, feared by all sailors, broke out among the men — scurvy! The hands and feet of the crew swelled, their gums grew over their teeth, so that they could not eat, they lay sick and dying . . . The storm bared its teeth.

"Take us back," the dying men groaned.

Da Gama turned grimly away. He hid the pain he felt at his crew's suffering. Onward he must go. To India, where eternal glory awaited them.

The storm broke. Darkness came. The sea tossed the little fleet about as a monster its prey. The men despaired of life now, unless their commander turned back.

Da Gama knew well that their fears were just, but his will was iron. Life without glory meant nothing to him.

"Turn about! Take us back to Portugal," clamored the crew, as the cold rains beat upon their heads.

Da Gama faced them. "When we left Belem," he said, "I promised in my heart not to turn back a foot of the way. On!"

"Mercy," pleaded his officers.

"Away!"

A sailor came running up. "The water is rushing in near the keel," he gasped.

"To the pumps!"

An officer approached. "We are running very low in provisions."

"Cut down the rations!"

All around death stared. The men no longer took heed of their lives. The sea lashed them from above and below. But a little while longer and the few brave souls who had dared the angry waters of the Cape would have disappeared from the surface; the vast un-conquered sea would have swallowed the frail ships like a wild animal, swallowing four morsels of food. The ships pitched violently. The sailors could hardly keep their footing.

"Take courage," shouted da Gama above the thundering din. "We are destined for glory. Even the sea trembles at us."

All at once through the black sky a ray of sun shone. The sea grew calm. The storm ceased. The ships sailed along peacefully. The men could hardly believe their happiness.

"What is it?" they asked, rubbing their eyes at the miracle.

"We have rounded the Cape," said da Gama.

The cry of "Land! Land!" arose. It was Mossel Bay, already discovered by their countryman Diaz, the land of the penguins which have no feathers on their wings and which bray like asses.

On they sailed, without lingering. Da Gama could not rest until India was reached. He was now in seas no European had ever sailed before. On Christmas Day he found land which he named "Natal." Past the island of Mozambique, past Mombasa, up to Malindi they sailed. Here beckoned friendly white-washed houses, coco palms, hop gardens. And da Gama let his weary crew rest awhile.

The King of Malindi welcomed the foreigners, exchanging presents with da Gama, sending provisions to his ships, and entertaining his guests with music. It was tempting to sport in this sunny spot of Africa, but da Gama was impatient. Regretfully, the crew set sail again. Again the vast sea and boundless sky. A week went by. Another week. Another week. Then the tired watch blinked his eyes and saw something.

"Land" he bellowed.

The whole crew rushed on deck. The dim form of mountains, like shadows, rose up from the sea. Da Gama gazed.

"India!" he cried exultingly.

IV

The longest journey ever made on the sea up to that time was over. Eleven months after he had sailed from Belem, Vasco da Gama reached Calicut, India.

To da Gama, whose nerves were taut with months of straining on the waste sea, Calicut was refreshingly alive. In its harbor was crowded every kind of oriental craft: Chinese junk, Arab schooner, native scow — hull touching hull. And the port itself was bewildering in its activity. It was a mart for all manner of trade. And this, above all, overjoyed the Europeans. For spices, drugs, and precious stones they had risked their lives. Not in vain, it seemed. The air of Calicut felt heavy with spices; the neck of every beggar looked to be hung with pearls.

"Peace go with you!" muttered a crouched form. "Give alms — for the charitable man is loved by all. Give alms!"

Over there a throng was gaping at the miracles of a fakir. He was caked with dirt and a human skull hung at his girdle.

"He eats live coals, or glass," da Gama was told. "A

risky business! But he has the powers of a magician. Presently you will see him conjure up a rope from the thin air, climb up, and disappear into the clouds."

Yonder, a row of merchants' stalls.

"Fish! Boiled fish! Best in Calicut."

"Buy your cloth here!" Calico, the Europeans called the Calicut cloth.

"Figs! Fig leaves! Coconuts!"

"Boiled rice! Delicious rice! Ah!" the vender bit into a coin that a customer handed him.

A dervish was shouting his lesson at the merchants in the stalls, "By the fig and the olive, the desire of making money keeps you busy until the grave. Later, you will realize your folly . . ."

Da Gama came upon a storyteller, seated on the ground, his legs tucked under him, stroking his long black beard and droning, ". . . lo, the earth trembled, and from the upper air descended upon Sindbad a person of enormous size, like a great palm tree. His eyes were two blazes of fire, and he had tusks like the tusks of swine, and lips like the lips of a camel, and the nails of his hands . . ."

To the court of the ruler went da Gama. The rajah, as he was called, was lying on a green velvet couch under a gilt canopy. A small man he was, with a dark beard. He listened courteously to the sturdy sea captain's tale — how for sixty years the Portuguese had been struggling to find a way to India.

"My soothsayers," said the rajah, "have warned me that some day India will be ruled by a prince of the West. Yet you are welcome. King Manuel is my brother, and all the Europeans are our brothers. This is a lucky day for you. Our country holds great riches. Spices and precious stones will be our gift to you."

"And to you, O Rajah," replied da Gama, "we shall bring gold and silver, corals and scarlet cloth."

Three months da Gama stayed in India, and then back he went to Portugal with his great news. He knew he had discovered the ocean way to India. But he did not know he had changed human history.

After two years, the people of Portugal had despaired of ever again seeing the fleet of adventurers. And now the four ships dotted the horizon of Belem once more. What if of the one hundred seventy men who had left only fifty-five returned . . . ?

Dom Manuel could not do enough to express his gratitude. Vasco da Gama was made one of his greatest noblemen. He was now Dom Vasco — and the Admiral of the Portuguese possessions in India. The greatest Portuguese poet of the time, Camoëns, celebrated the life of the Portuguese hero in his famous epic poem, the "Lusiads."

Ferdinand Magellan

(c. 1480–1521)

AROUND THE WORLD

I

FERDINAND MAGELLAN, Portuguese sea captain and adventurer, received a letter from his friend Francisco Serrano. Magellan had left his friend prowling around somewhere in the Indian Ocean, while he had sailed back to Lisbon.

"I have discovered," said the letter, "a new world, larger and richer than that found by Vasco da Gama, the Spice Islands! I shall remain here, for the native king has made me his captain-general . . ."

The Spice Islands, about which such strange tales had reached Portugal! Here were supposed to live men with spurs on their ankles, hogs with horns, hens that laid their eggs nine feet underground, boiling rivers, poisonous crabs, giant oysters, pearls as large as rocks, and tons of spices.

Since he had renounced his nationality, Magellan went to young Charles V, King of Spain.

"Fit me out a fleet," offered Magellan, "and the Spiceries are yours."

Like Columbus, he explained, he would sail west.

On the other side of South America stretched a new ocean which Balboa had seen a few years before. There must be a strait, held Magellan, cleaving through the continent from the east to this ocean.

"And westward on this ocean must be the Spice Islands and my friend Francisco." He wanted as much to see his friend Serrano as to blaze the westward way across the world. They had been shipmates together, had starved and made merry together, and were bosom friends. So Magellan would risk danger to come to his friend.

Charles was willing enough that this great adventurer should strike out to the Spiceries in this new way. But the old trouble again appeared in mustering a crew. Who was foolhardy enough to throw his life away? Brave men are not easy to find.

Magellan himself did not think twice about the danger, for his heroism was famous. Everybody knew how he had saved the lives of an entire crew, and how he never seemed to care much for his own skin.

From here and from there at length a crew was chosen. Nearly three hundred men, all sizes, shapes, and nationalities. Five old ships there were, with ribs said to be as soft as butter.

"A week at sea," people warned Magellan, "and the rotten boards will split asunder and leave you drowning like rats."

Magellan listened politely, thanked them all for the sound advice, and went about his business firmly. One of his ships was called *Victoria* — "Victory." This was the motto he would wave around the world.

II

Colder and colder it grew, and fearfully stormy. The fleet was tossing about helplessly in a gale so fierce that it wrecked the ships' forecastles. Magellan saw he could not go on. He must seek a harbor in which to take shelter for the winter. Suddenly a pleasant coast came into view and toward it Magellan steered.

At once a cry arose, "Back to Spain! Back to Spain!"

"No, my men," declared Magellan, "we shall not go back. Never until we have done what we set out to do—reached the Spice Islands. Here, in this new land, we stay until spring thaws the ice. But already we are farther south than any other navigator has sailed. Courage!"

"But where are we? The country seems uninhabited by man." They saw in this strange country a bird resembling an ostrich, the South American rhea, and some rabbits and foxes.

And a strange and beautiful animal appeared on a slope. It was about four feet high, with a gracefully curved neck, and long slender legs. Above, its silky hair was fawn-colored; below, pure white.

"What is it?" asked the wondering sailors. Europeans had never seen such an animal. Later they named it *guanaco*.

The animal bounded away and an Indian of huge stature appeared on the slope. He stopped, stared at the white men, and then approaching, struck up acquaintance. He towered well over six feet. Presently he went to bring some other Indians.

The group of tall Indians approached the Spaniards, who felt that they hardly reached the chests of the Indians. The natives were clad in skins of the *guanaco* skillfully sewed together. Their feet were shod in moccasins made from the same kind of skins. Those made their feet seem very large.

Someone whispered to Magellan, "Haven't they enormous feet?"

It was the country of big feet. Big-feeters, Magellan called the inhabitants — Patagones — and the name has remained.

To the Spaniards, the Indians seemed happy giants, always singing and dancing. But what an appetite! Magellan invited two of them for a snack, a mere nibble, that they might talk or make signs at each other about the straits the adventurer was seeking. That was a great mistake, and a calamity to the crew, who were running short of food. For, while Magellan munched on two or three biscuits, the two guests ate up a basketful, and daintily washed it down with half a bucket of water.

"We know nothing of any straits around here," the Patagonians signaled.

So, when the season grew milder, Magellan sailed away from Patagonia. After months of exploring the southern end of South America, Magellan suddenly came upon a vast inlet. As the expedition wandered into these new waters, it dawned on Magellan that he was in the long-sought strait — the Strait of Magellan, as it is now known.

Fortune was smiling now, thought Magellan, but his men were flinching.

"No one has ever sailed that ocean on the other side of this strait," they argued. "Who knows its perils or its extent or its course? Our provisions are low. We can go no farther. Let us turn back."

Magellan faced them. "My men," he said, "you are right. The voyage will be long and dangerous. Our provisions are wasted. But believe that you are heroes, that the world will never forget you if you succeed in your adventure. For myself, I would rather have to eat the leather on our ships' yards than turn back. Will you continue with me, or return?"

"On! On! We will go on!" cheered the men. "We will sail with you to the other side of the globe!"

As they sailed westward through the strait, Magellan gave names to all the capes, bays, inlets, mountains, and harbors. To the south lay a land of mountains on whose tops were seen burning fires. Land of Fire, Magellan called it — Tierra del Fuego.

All at once before his hungry eyes lay the waters of the great ocean seen by Balboa seven years before. With tears of joy and salutes from his cannon, Magellan greeted it.

As the ships swung into the new ocean, the fierce winds died down into a gentle breeze, the heaving waters became peaceful. Thus it continued. Magellan was overjoyed at the change. "A pacific ocean!" he exclaimed.

His joy was short-lived; the food supply was dwindling fast. The faces of the crew became pinched, their eyes watery. And in the starved company broke out the scurvy. Weak with hunger, they offered no resistance to the terrible disease. By dozens the crew perished.

The survivors envied the dead. Food! It was a nightmare with them, with Magellan as well as the rest. No fish could be caught, and no more meat was left. There were no more mealtimes. Each man caught a rat if he could or devoured a biscuit which swarmed with worms.

"I would rather have to eat leather than turn back." Magellan remembered these words. Alas, they had been prophetic. He ordered the crew to cut the hides from the main yards and boil them. When they had no more leather, they would eat sawdust.

One morning the half-dead crew awoke to a strange sound on the water—human voices! They looked out, spellbound. There on the shining waters were swarms of canoes filled with brown men holding aloft stalks of bananas and clusters of coconuts. With a cry, the famished crew fell upon the fruits and nuts while their visitors looked on amazed.

In the distance Magellan saw one of the most beautiful sights in the world — island mountains. Forests rose up before him, of bamboos and palms. As he gazed, one of his officers ran up, saying, "Those rascals have stolen our small boat."

"Ah, we are among thieves," said Magellan. "Let us call these lands the Robber Islands — Ladrones."

At one of these islands, Guam, he landed and refreshed his men, although he stayed but two days. The Spiceries must be somewhere in these waters, and he must be off to seek them. His bosom friend Francisco awaited him there, and he longed to embrace him, and to say to him that the sight of his dear Francisco was worth all the suffering he had endured.

A week more on the sea and land loomed up. His heart leaped, but in a vain joy, for this new group of islands was not the Spiceries at all. What were they? Magellan took out his map of the world, but he did not find them on it. So he sketched in his new discovery — and the Philippines became a part of the globe. The islands were beautiful with palm trees and clear springs. "Here," thought Magellan, "I can help the sick among my crew to recover." With his own hands he proceeded to tend them.

For a whole day not a human being appeared on the horizon. Magellan was becoming curious when, from one of the neighboring islands, a boat manned by nine natives pushed off. Were they friends? The doubt lasted only until the boat touched the shore of Magellan's camp. The native leader stepped forward with joyous greeting, and gifts were exchanged between the East and the West. Red caps, and bells, and looking glasses were the gifts of the men of the West. The East was more practical. It supplied the famished adventurers with fish, bananas, and a strange fruit at which Magellan marveled, for it was bread, milk, and oil all in one, he thought — the coconut!

"Come to dinner," invited the native hosts cordially in sign language.

Food was what most interested men who had just come through a starvation period.

"Since we were not prepared for your visit," gesticulated the native king, "you will have to do with our usual simple food."

The first course was an enormous portion of roast pork. The service was entirely of gold — platters and cups of solid gold — and golden plaques and panels blazed brilliantly from the walls, dazzling the eyes and hearts of the Europeans . . . But on with the dinner! The main dish consisted of quantities of rice with spiced pork, sauce, and gravy. The beverages were especially delightful — a soothing drink prepared from the milk of the coconut, and a mild palm wine.

"This dinner was worth the trip," thought the adventurers with satisfaction. "We won't want food for six months more."

All at once a huge platter of roast fish and ginger was served. The Westerners began to feel alarmed. After all, the capacity of the human stomach is limited. But could a guest refuse? Taking heart, for they were brave men, they attacked the fish and by sheer courage disposed of it.

"The danger is past," they thought faintly.

But wait . . . The enemy was advancing with fresh power. Platters of fish and rice steamed in. Recklessly the Europeans fell upon the dish — and collapsed. But so did the king of the islands. And they all snored away the effects of the food.

The king was a strange specimen to Magellan. "A savage!" thought the commander. "Look at him! Tawny in color, his body painted and nearly naked; gold rings in his ears, gold studs in his teeth. He is short and fat, a lover of ease and quiet. Though he is a just man, he is also arrogant; nobody may speak to him except through a tube. His Royalty must not stoop; therefore when he has occasion to enter a room with a low doorway, he has to go by way of the roof. Such queer customs, too! For instance, to show his affection for you, he shoots out his clenched fist at you. And when he is old, he will be thrust aside unceremoniously and his children placed in command. What savages!"

And the native probably thought: "What strange people these Spaniards are! So parched-looking, and as skinny as skeletons! Why did they risk their lives to come here? Isn't their home comfortable? How impressed they were with that metal, gold! They seemed to worship it. The worst of them is their uninteresting faces. There is no 'make-up' on them, no life — just the skin of an animal with no art on it to make it human. And their bodies they cover all up with rags, as if they would shun the air and sunshine. Such queer customs, too. To show affection each squeezes the other's palm."

The image of the Spice Islands, now called the Moluccas, and his friend Francisco made Magellan restless. It was time to leave the pleasant haunts of the Philippines.

III

One day, about three years after Magellan left Spain, the people of Seville saw a singular ship wearily making its way up the Guadalquivir. So battered was it that even the ghostly emblem it bore, *Victoria,* failed to make it recognizable. Straining in every joint, the ship anchored at last as the curious crowd stared from the dock. A few faces on deck seemed familiar.

With a cry of surprise, the watchers exclaimed, "It must be Magellan's *Victoria!* Where is the rest of the fleet? Where is Magellan?"

Juan del Cano stepped forward, pale and cadaverous

as a specter. "Our leader is dead," he said sadly, "buried in the Philippines. Of the two hundred and eighty men who started full of hope from San Lucar, only eighteen of us are returning; of five ships, only one."

The crowd rushed on board to embrace the eighteen heroes, and to mourn with them the loss of Magellan.

"But," said del Cano, brightening, "we have found the Spiceries, which were Magellan's goal . . . When we left the Philippines, with anguish at our great loss, we sailed to Borneo, which is the largest island in the world. After staying awhile in the wonderful palace of the sultan, over the Celebes Sea we rode straight to the Spiceries, to the Isles of Ternate and Tidore.

"We asked for Francisco Serrano to sadden him with news of the death of his best friend. But it was unnecessary. It seemed as though the two friends were bound in death as in life. The shadow of death had no sooner fallen upon Magellan in the Philippines than it hastened to take his friend, too, on the island of Ternate."

There was little more to tell. Homeward the *Victoria* had sailed, by way of Vasco da Gama's water, around the Cape of Good Hope, up the West coast of Africa, straight to Spain. Clear around the globe of the earth the eighteen heroes had gone.

With this journey, all further guesses about the shape of the earth were made unnecessary. Magellan and his comrades swept aside the myths of an Atlas upholding the world on his shoulders, of a flat ocean from whose edge you fell headlong, and similar fearsome tales. This first circumnavigation of the globe showed that the world is round.

The world's debt to Magellan, the one who gave us

this proof, will be remembered as long as ships sail through the Strait of Magellan, and men glance skyward. For in the heavens of the southern hemisphere, two star clusters have been named the Magellanic Clouds.

James Cook

(1728–1779)

THE SOUTH SEAS

I

THE members of the Royal Society of England were agitated. Their calculations showed that in the near future an exciting event was to happen in the heavens. On June 3, 1769, the planet Venus, sailing in the sky, was to come between the earth and the sun, passing right across the sun's disc. An awesome and striking sight it would be, but that was not the reason it was important.

"If we knew the time it takes Venus to cross the sun," announced the Society, "we could figure other facts from it; for instance, how far the sun is from us. We must station observers in many locations on the earth, in such far lands as Norway, Northern Canada, and particularly on one of the islands in the south Pacific Ocean. Then, with calculations based on indirect measurement, the distance of the earth to the sun can be calculated more accurately than has ever been done before. You must send someone," the Society appealed to the British Government, "for this event will not occur again for over a hundred years. The knowledge we will gain from these observations, we hope will eventually enable us to compute the longitude of any place on the globe as accurately as we now can its latitude."

The Royal Navy was interested. "This might mean," it reasoned, "that the captain of a ship will be able to figure the position of his ship at sea." The Navy decided to supply the ship the Society needed, and also its captain — James Cook.

James Cook, a farm boy with negligible schooling, had served his apprenticeship as a sailor on the freight ships of a coal company. During the seven years he worked for the company he devoted every spare moment to the study of navigation and chart-making. He became expert at sailing through the tricky currents close to the English coast, and it did not take long for the owner of the company to recognize Cook's remarkable ability. Thereupon James Cook was given more difficult duties, and eventually he was made the master of a ship.

Nevertheless, James Cook was unhappy. Distant lands and strange peoples had always lured him. He parted reluctantly from his employer and joined the Royal Navy as an able seaman. The captains and the admirals soon discovered the talents of this tall, quiet sailor, and he was promoted to master of a ship. He was now discharging duties that were both difficult and dangerous. England and France were then at war. James Cook's order was to chart the treacherous channel of the St. Lawrence River directly opposite the French camp. He had to take soundings during the night to evade observation. For several nights he carried on the work unmolested. One night he was discovered by the French, who sent a number of canoes filled with their Indian allies to surround him. Cook leaped from the bow and escaped just as the Indians entered by the stern and carried the canoe off.

Through the long winter evenings, when the ice had thickened and the ship lay at anchor, there was little activity on board. Cook would busy himself studying geometry and navigation by the feeble candlelight. There was no one to turn to for explanations, so he had to work everything out by himself.

James Cook soon put his astronomy to use. He had calculated that an eclipse of the sun would be visible from Newfoundland on August 5, 1766. Since he was close to Newfoundland, he used his telescope and chronometer. When he returned to England that fall, he sent a carefully written report of his observation to the Royal Society. The members of the Society commented that he was "a good mathematician, and very expert in his business."

II

In August of 1768 Cook, with eighty-four men, sailed away from England in a vessel modestly named the *Endeavour*. Besides noting the transit of Venus in an unknown region, he had been bidden by the Navy to explore the entire area. "We think there is a continent somewhere in the South Seas," said geographers. "There must be a vast continent in the southern hemisphere to counterbalance Europe and other lands in the northern hemisphere. Magellan once passed through a strait at the tip of South America. Perhaps a continent lies south of that strait."

As the *Endeavour* sailed to Rio de Janeiro, and then to the southern tip of South America, the fantastically strange life that teems in the sea was closely studied. Cook was no ordinary sea captain, and did not have to be told to keep his eyes open. He was by nature keenly interested in scientific things.

"Flying fish," wrote Cook in a letter, "have appeared to us, darting gracefully across the water. Their sides have the color and brightness of burnished silver."

As they sailed on, the sea seemed to emit flashes like lightning. What caused this? The sailors cast nets and brought up a kind of jellyfish, which looked like metal in a white heat. With these medusae, as they are called, were caught some small crabs shining like glow-worms.

Doubling Cape Horn, even in a heavy sea and wild gale, was no mighty effort for so skilled a navigator as Cook. The *Endeavour* steered for Tahiti, the island from which the scientists were to view the heavens. There was one cause for anxiety. Suppose the morning of June 3, 1769, dawned murky and the clouds hid the sport of the stars? The perilous journey would have been undertaken in vain.

There was another anxious question. Would the natives of Tahiti be friendly to the strangers?

"The natives are to be treated with all kindness," Cook warned his crew sternly. "You have guns. Beware of turning them on human beings." He announced a set of rules that must be observed by everyone on the *Endeavour* in dealing with natives. The first rule was: "to endeavour, by every fair means, to cultivate a friendship with the natives, and to treat them with all imaginable humanity." And from then on to the end of his life he enforced these rules resolutely.

One great day Tahiti appeared out of the warm sea, a land of beauty, with rills that gathered in cool streams, hills soft in the tropical sun, and reefs of coral that shone brilliantly. Surrounded by green islets, the land seemed a fertile paradise.

Fear of the inhabitants proved unfounded. The natives came in canoes to meet them, bringing green branches of trees as tokens of peace and friendship. These the crew stuck in the rigging, to show that the English, too, were peaceful. With some of his men Captain Cook went ashore. The chief welcomed them, and gave them permission to set up their scientific instruments.

At every step the trees and the flowers, the butterflies and the fragrant earth delighted the sea-wearied men. During the next few weeks, while they waited for the third of June, Cook closely studied the customs of the Tahitians, and the plants and animals of the island. Every day the ship's scientist, Dr. Solander, went out in search of specimens.

The captain found the Tahitians a handsome dreamy race, cleanly in person and affable toward strangers. Of course, an Englishman and a Tahitian see things not quite the same way, and now and then a quarrel would arise. But Cook was always on the lookout. If ever his own men were at fault, he punished them; if ever the natives were, he reasoned with them.

A few times, indeed, it seemed as though serious trouble would break out between the two races. At those times the English crew were ready to put their cannon into action. But the captain did a strange thing: he forebade the use of firearms. Because he was a coward? Not at all. There was no braver soul alive than James Cook.

"They are stubborn and we must yield, because we are so much stronger than they. What do we gain by blowing a few creatures off the face of the earth? Their sticks are no match for our guns. Hold off!" So, with his tact and gentleness of soul, the captain smoothed out the rough spots of his relations with the Tahitians.

He did more than save the natives from the guns of his men, for he was no mere adventurer, this peace-loving captain. He gave them what was more valuable than gold. Tahiti was fertile, but did not produce many kinds of plant food. The captain, therefore, planted seeds which he had brought from South America, so that the Tahitians might enjoy the orange, the lemon, the lime, and the watermelon. For this the Tahitians loved him. They played for him their music with drums and flutes. They blew the latter with their nostrils. For "Captain Toote," as they called him in their soft, musical language, they danced and wrestled.

"I admire their spirit in athletics," said Cook. "The victor never crows about his superiority, and the vanquished never whines about his poor luck. They are sportsmen."

The names he gave the new places he discovered show the peaceful sentiments of Cook: "Society Islands," after the Royal Society that sent him on the expedition; "Mercury Bay," because in that bay he studied the planet Mercury; "Friendly Islands," to remember how cordially the natives welcomed him.

At last came the night of June second, the night before the eclipse of the sun by Venus. The scientists of the party could not sleep a wink for nervous excitement. "What if tomorrow be cloudy?" But the morrow dawned clear, the sun was there, waiting radiantly for Venus! At twenty-five minutes and twelve seconds after nine o'clock in the morning, a dark speck, the planet Venus, was seen on the edge of the sun. Eighteen minutes and twelve seconds later, the planet was completely inside the sun's rim. Slowly it crept across the face of the sun. The planet took more than six hours to make its transit.

The expedition had been successful. Captain Cook felt it had been worth the thousand hardships. Now he was free to look for the South Sea continent.

As the ship weighed anchor, the islanders rushed out to the shore to cry farewell. Chief Orie wept aloud. "Come back," he pleaded.

III

Nearly three months later at Mercury Bay, New Zealand, Red-smeared Dragon, a little boy of eight, was looking intently over the sea.

"Did you ever see such a big bird on the water?" he asked his playfellows. "What beautiful white wings it has!"

"Look!" cried one. "A smaller bird is descending from the big bird."

"It's coming toward us," added another.

"The small one is not a bird," slowly said Red-smeared Dragon. "It looks somewhat like a canoe."

The boys turned to a group of old men for advice.

"These are goblins," explained one sagely. "They are rowing with their backs to the land. Only goblins can do that, for they have eyes in the back of their heads."

As the goblins stepped on the beach, all fled fearfully to the thicket. But when the children, peeping from behind a tree, saw these wondrous beings walk peaceably about, pick up stones and grasses, they said, "Perhaps these goblins are not as wicked as our Maori goblins."

Timidly the children ventured from their hiding place. They lighted a fire for the goblins, and offered them sweet potatoes. But suddenly they saw a most amazing sight. One of these beings pointed a kind of walking staff at a cormorant perched on a tree. The stick flashed lightning. A thunderclap resounded. At the same instant the bird fell.

Frightened, the children fled. But when they heard the goblins laugh merrily, they took heart and returned to look at the fallen bird.

"The bird is dead," exclaimed Red-smeared Dragon.

"But what killed it?" his comrades wondered. "These goblins kill with thunderbolts."

The boat which Red-smeared Dragon and his friends had taken for a bird did not leave the bay, and one day, little Red-smeared Dragon and some of his friends were taken to it in a canoe. Wrapped in their flax coats, they sat close together on the deck, fearing to move. If the goblins should bewitch them they would never see their homes again.

Red-smeared Dragon's sharp eyes missed nothing. He easily made out the leader of the goblins, who was grave and dignified. This goblin walked up to Red-smeared Dragon and his friends. After patting the boys' heads he took from his pocket a large nail. The boys sat motionless. At last Red-smeared Dragon looked up at the goblin captain. His eyes were so kind that Red-smeared Dragon laughingly held out his hand, and the nail was his!

When the children went home, they agreed that the goblin captain was a *tino rangatira* — a perfect gentleman and a great chief. His precious nail Red-smeared Dragon carried as a charm around his neck. And that is how a Maori boy remembered Captain Cook's visit to New Zealand.

IV

Cook was still searching for the continent said to be somewhere in the South Seas. But he had seen no such land. "I do not find a trace of ocean currents," he reasoned, "and that means that no continent is near." Only islands dotted the ocean, some of them only lagoons surrounded by reefs and coconut palms.

When he reached New Zealand, map makers still believed that the South Sea continent existed; but Captain Cook was skeptical. From Poverty Bay in New Zealand, he sailed south following the shore. In the course of time he found himself back in Poverty Bay. No, this was not the South Sea continent. It was an island, two islands in fact. Within six months' time Cook had charted the twenty-four hundred miles of New Zealand's coast line; and then, from a point he called Cape Farewell, he sailed away to the west.

To the eastern coast of New Holland, now called Australia, a land then practically unknown, Captain Cook steered his ship. All he knew about New Holland was that a few European vessels had touched it. Along the coast of Australia he sighted some natives, their bodies decorated with streaks of white paint, fishing.

Once in a harbor, he landed for fresh water and fuel. Here for several days the ship's botanist, Joseph Banks, was busy gathering countless specimens of new flowers and plants, and studying trees that were unknown to the scientists of Europe. "Botany Bay," Cook named the harbor.

As he continued northward, he mapped the bays, islands, capes and rivers he saw. Everywhere he examined the plant and animal life. He was a scientist-explorer.

He came to the sand banks and the coral reefs of the Great Barrier Reef. In and out of the islands he kept weaving, at great danger to the ship and crew, for there were constant threats of shoals and coral rocks. Once, indeed, the *Endeavour* did strike a concealed sharp and jagged rock of coral, which put a nasty hole in her keel. For twenty-four hours it looked as though they would go under. The vessel was caught. Every part of the rock was so rough as to grind away whatever rubbed against it, even with the gentlest of motions. Only the resolute, quiet manner of the captain, and the loyalty his men bore him, saved their lives. Under the most trying circumstances they managed to mend the leak.

"Why must we risk our lives in this useless way?" grumbled some of the men.

Cook pointed to his charts and his notebook. "How else," said he, "could we describe all these islands or study the continent behind them? How else could we help our scientists in their study of plants? And how could we help the sailors of the future more than by showing them which are the navigable parts of these waters?"

Captain James Cook succeeded beyond expectation. He had studied the transit of Venus. He had proved New Zealand to be two large islands. He had shown that there was no South Sea continent near Tahiti. He had explored the eastern coast of Australia. All these discoveries he had put on the most accurately charted maps of the century. What greater achievement could any explorer boast?

"I have not lost one man by sickness during the whole voyage," he said. And that pleased him most.

V

The Royal Society was again worried. "There are so many islands in the South Seas; there must be a continent, too. Perhaps it is much farther south of Tahiti than we had at first thought."

No one better than Cook could be chosen to settle the question. "His charts of New Zealand are extraordinary," said geographers. "Very few parts even of the coast of neighboring France are so carefully drawn as is this remote coast."

The captain was ready. He had been studying the problem and how to meet the greatest enemy of men at sea — scurvy. The old captains — Vasco da Gama, Magellan, and Henry Hudson — had seen their men perish miserably from scurvy. Every long voyage meant scurvy. From the time that he joined the Navy, he watched men become ill, with sores and bleeding gums. Ships reeked of death and the sick. The stricken wailed and lamented unceasingly.

"Scurvy is not due to the climate and the winds," he thought. "Eating only salt meat and hardtack must be the cause. Plenty of vegetables will cure scurvy — celery, sauerkraut, peas, carrots." Vegetables were served every day on the captain's table. The captain had set the example. Soon all the men on board ship began to eat vegetables regularly.

He was right. During his last voyage, which took him around the world on a three-year cruise of over sixty thousand miles, he lost only one man out of one hundred and eighteen. The specter of scurvy was laid.

On this voyage Cook hoped to settle definitely the question of the southern continent. He intended to explore waters that no European had ever before sailed. He would sail as close to the Antarctic Circle as he could. Being a true geographer, he had another purpose in mind: to observe the inhabitants of whatever islands he came upon, and win their friendship.

He began by venturing farther south than any other

sailor had dared. The cold became intense, and the polar gales swept the decks with seas. Icebergs loomed through fog like spectral cliffs. The sea hammered their sides. Cook picked his course cautiously. To be caught on the weather side of an iceberg in a rough sea meant being smashed to bits.

The ship approached an ice floe which extended as far as the eye could see. In vain Cook tried to sail around it. Ice fields filled the horizon. The sailors' hands bled from the intense cold. Was there a continent farther south? It was foolhardy to go on. The cold had become unbearable. Cook, therefore, steered north for New Zealand.

He could not resist revisiting old scenes and old friends in sunny Tahiti. The good King Orie, when he heard of Cook's arrival, ran out, threw his arms about him, and wept for joy.

"I have brought you something," said Cook. He led ashore three cows and one bull, a horse and mare, two rams and ten sheep. "These will be very useful in time," he promised. Then he planted roots — potatoes, turnips, parsnips, carrots — and taught the islanders how to cultivate them.

Another might have returned to England to announce that there was no South Sea continent. Not Captain Cook. There were still some parts of the ocean near the Antarctic Circle he had not explored. To be thorough, he would again have to strike south, and his crew would again suffer torturing cold and the dangers of icebergs. Yet such was the confidence of his men that they cheerfully followed him again among the icebergs and treacherous Antarctic currents. And finally, James Cook proved beyond a doubt that no continent existed in the South Seas.

In a third voyage to the Pacific Ocean he discovered the Hawaiian Islands. To insure further his claim as the greatest explorer of the century, he cruised along Oregon to the Bering Strait, probing a Northwest Passage from the Atlantic Ocean.

To Captain James Cook the world owes much. He solved great geographical problems, and he spread the seeds of civilization to new regions of the globe.

Henry Creswicke Rawlinson

(1810–1895)

A LOST WORLD FOUND

I

A PERSON traveling in the East might find himself among the ruins of Persepolis, a flourishing city two thousand years ago. He would wonder at the decorated tombs — no doubt the tombs of kings — and at the moldering remains of a great palace, with only a few high columns still standing to remind him of its former glory. As he gazes at the silent ruins of the "Persian City," once the busy capital of the mightiest empire of the world, he might sigh, "Thus passes the glory of the world."

The walls and monuments, he would notice, are covered with curious wedge-shaped designs. "What are these? Decorations, perhaps."

A few travelers in the year 1802 were very curious about these wedge-shaped decorations. They copied them in order to study them more carefully in Europe.

In Göttingen, Germany, Georg Grotefend, a teacher of Greek, was shown the peculiar wedge-shaped marks. His friends knew that no one was quicker at solving puzzles than Grotefend. When he examined these marks, he noticed a strange thing. All the "decorations" looked alike! What in the world were they? Perhaps letters in some language, long forgotten.

"But how can I learn this forgotten language, when I don't know a single letter? If I only had a clue . . ." He glanced over the strange characters . . . "What's this?" he exclaimed. He could make out a single group of signs — no doubt a word. This word occurred again and again. "What word would a king use on his monuments so often? Either his name — or the word 'king.' I have it! It must be 'king.' "

He continued his study. "Here's the same word again, but with another ending. That must be 'kings.' Here these two words are side by side. That probably means 'King of Kings'!"

The scholar could have danced for joy. He knew that the old Persian kings liked to boast of their greatness. He knew that each called himself "King of Kings." That was his clue.

The word which he believed to be "king" he found in the first line, and with it another word. "This might be 'great,' " he reasoned. "The phrase would then read 'Great King.' "

He looked at other copies of inscriptions. They all seemed to be worded in the same way, "Great King, 'Great King.' "

So far, so good. Again he took up the paper. What could he now discover? He peered at the paper. Nothing new. His face fell. Just as he was putting it aside, he thought, "Here is a king. He erects a monument, celebrating something or other — most likely a victory over his enemies. He called himself 'Great King, King of Kings.' What else would he write? What else?

"His name!"

With this new possibility in mind, Grotefend lifted the paper. His hand trembled. The first word, which was unfamiliar, was followed by the familiar phrase. The first word might, therefore, be the king's name!

His eye traveled farther down. Again the phrase he knew. And before this, another unfamiliar word. "This might be another king's name. Suppose I call the king whose name is first on the paper King X. Then the first line reads, 'X, Great King, King of Kings!' " He studied his wedge-shaped characters. " 'X, Great King, King of Kings . . . Y, King.' The missing word must be — let's see — 'son'?"

He read the words again: " 'X, Great King, King of Kings, son of Y, King.' I am making progress! At this rate, I'll soon know the characters of the Old Persian language, dead for two thousand years."

Farther on he read, " 'Y, Great King, King of Kings, son of . . . King.' "

"I have it! I have it! This inscription contains the names of three Persian rulers — grandfather, father, and son. Now, there were only twelve Persian kings, and if I'm right that these three in the inscription were grandfather, father, and son, I can rule out a few of the twelve . . . Let's see . . . Hystaspes, Darius, Xerxes. How do these names correspond with the Persian text? The first is longer — as it should be."

II

In 1827, Henry Creswicke Rawlinson, a boy of seventeen, had gone out to India in the service of the East India Company. All he knew of the strange wedge-shaped characters of Persia was that they were a hopeless puzzle. He had never heard of Grotefend and his work.

Since he learned languages very easily, he was soon able to understand several of the languages spoken in India. He spoke the modern Persian language almost as well as a native. Unlike his comrades in the service, Rawlinson found time to do a great deal of reading, especially in history. At one time he was arrested because of his love for books. He had bought more books than he could pay for; he owed the book dealer nearly one hundred dollars.

Rawlinson's curiosity was aroused by the ruins of the ancient world around him. In 1837 he journeyed to Persia, where he came to a remarkable rock, five hundred feet high, at Behistun. On the steep face of this rock was hewn, three hundred feet up, an inscription which Rawlinson was eager to study. But the way up the rock was bare and slippery. A foot ledge had been constructed by the workers in ancient times to enable them to carve the monument. Now, after so many thousands of years, the foot ledge was weatherworn and slippery. One false step would have hurled him down the precipice. But he possessed a keen eye, a cool head, and a sure foot.

Three and four times a day, for many a day, Rawlinson climbed the three hundred feet without the aid of rope or ladder — without any help at all. On reaching the ledge, he steadied his body against the rock with his left arm. In his left hand he held a notebook, his right hand was busy with the pencil. At the risk of his life he copied the inscription of about four hundred lines.

Now he set to work on the mystery of the wedge-shaped signs. His eager eyes saw a word occurring again and again. This inscription, he reasoned, was engraved by order of some king. It must therefore be the Persian word for "king."

The method that Grotefend used, Rawlinson used also: "Here's the same word again, but with an ending. The words are side by side. The phrase must mean 'King of Kings.' "

The same list of kings that Grotefend puzzled out occurred to Henry Rawlinson. And Rawlinson, with no knowledge of that pioneer's work, hit upon the same list of kings. "Hystaspes, Darius, Xerxes . . . How do these names fit? The first name is longer than the others — as it should be."

At this point Grotefend had stopped. Rawlinson, however, was just beginning. By dint of great perseverance, he worked out for himself the entire alphabet of the Old Persian language.

He discovered that the inscription had been placed on the rock by Darius, king of Persia, who wanted the world to marvel at his mighty deeds. The rock stands on the great highway between Persia and Babylonia and can be seen for many miles. In the inscription, the king recounts how he defeated numerous rebels and conquered many nations. Above the inscription is engraved the picture of King Darius, who stands with his right hand saluting the god Ahura-Mazda, his left hand resting on one end of a bow, and his foot trampling an enemy.

When Rawlinson sent a translation to the Royal Asiatic Society of London, great enthusiasm arose in Europe. Learned societies honored him. Everybody agreed that although his work had been carried out under greater difficulties than that of any European scholar, he had surpassed them all.

Studying the inscription further, Rawlinson could make out what seemed to be two other systems of writing besides the Old Persian that he could read. "There may be three languages here. King Darius probably wanted all the nations of his great empire to understand what is written on this stone." Having deciphered and translated the Old Persian, he now set himself to the task of working out the other two languages. As a result two more languages, the Babylonian language and that of the land of Elam, are known to us.

Inspired by his great work, scholars were now able to decipher the curious wedge-shaped writing, which they called "cuneiform." By 1853 archaeologists had uncovered in Persia and Babylonia the written remains of a vast civilization, before undreamed of.

Many people still doubted. "You say that you can read the cuneiform writing," they said. "But if we were to give the same writing to different scholars, each one would translate it differently."

"Test us," calmly suggested Rawlinson.

From the ruins of a temple a clay cylinder was dug up. Four different scholars were given copies of it. "Translate it," was the order.

The result was the glory of Rawlinson's work. All four, none knowing the version of the other three scholars, gave the same translation, which turned out to be the story of a king who ruled long before David was king of Israel.

The doubting world was now convinced, and Rawlinson kept on with his work. It was not easy. The clay tablets were often found shattered in a hundred particles, and to fit the tiny fragments together correctly was harder than any jigsaw puzzle. Then, the writing was small and so worn down that even a magnifying glass would fail at times to bring out an uncertain letter. After the shattered particles of clay were set into their original form, and the cuneiform letters were made out, came the most difficult task of all: to decipher the new words.

Rawlinson set for himself two great projects. He would translate these ancient documents so the world could read them, and he would lead an expedition to the East to uncover other ruins of the past. The British Museum in London became his workshop.

There Rawlinson, who was now acknowledged as the leading authority on cuneiform writing, pored over the faint inscriptions of three thousand years ago. Since the time he had shown the world the meaning of the wedge-shaped symbols, archaeologists had dug up a mass of baked clay cylinders and tablets, boundary stones, bricks — all with cuneiform writing on them. From the ruins of Babylon, Nineveh, and other ancient cities, these were shipped to the British Museum for Rawlinson to decipher.

When these constant reminders from Bagdad and from Persia had made him long for the East he loved, and for his Persian and Arab friends, he left London to lead an expedition into the past.

He showed himself to be an expert archaeologist. He knew just where to excavate for relics of ancient times. What could be more exciting than digging up a statue, a glass, a piece of ivory thousands of years old? On lucky days the archaeologist struck the temple of an ancient god or the treasures of a king; on bad days, nothing.

Once Rawlinson was examining a large heap of clay tablets. "It seems I have discovered an Assyrian library!" he exclaimed. The more he read the ancient writing, the more amazed he was. "Here is an Assyrian grammar, and here a book on science. What is this? Something we have been hoping to find, a table of Assyrian weights and measures! Now we shall understand their systems of measure. And here are all the other books that should be in a library — books on history, geography, and astronomy." With what care he packed the fragile clay books to be shipped to the British Museum!

Every moment he could spare from his duties and from his working on the cuneiform mystery of the Behistun Rock was devoted to the geography of the region where he was stationed: Persia, or Iran as it is called today.

"I am not ready to be a geographer," he said, "until I

have studied all the accounts of the lands I shall explore." It did not matter to him whether the geography was written in Greek, Latin, Arabic or Persian, for he knew them all. And, because a geographer must know how to make maps, he learned how.

What interested him most were the obscure and rarely visited ruins of Persia. He wondered what ancient towns were once there. "What trade routes led through the town?" he would ask himself. "What was the town's name then? Perhaps some Persian traveler wrote about this region. I shall find out by looking through Persian manuscripts."

Rawlinson's keen eye saw through the ruins to the old-time stirring town, and his knowledge of the ancient geography of the country enriched the world's knowledge of the East. He became not only the foremost scholar on cuneiform writing but also England's authority on Central Asia. The Royal Geographical Society elected him president. Whether it was the question of the best route for an overland telegraph line from Constantinople to Karachi, or the trade routes between Turkestan and India, Rawlinson knew the answer. For he had linked his geography of the present to his dream of the past.

III

Let us wander through the Babylon that Rawlinson conjured up for us, in the days of Nebuchadnezzar when Babylon was in its glory.

As we journey through the flat Babylonian countryside — a land of little rain — we cannot help but admire the web of canals that irrigate the fertile fields. There are great waterways which connect the rivers Euphrates and Tigris, and there are branch canals that carry off the surplus water to smaller irrigation canals wherever water is needed. The Babylonian king boasts of his public works: the system of canals, and equally important, their maintenance — preventing them from becoming filled with silt.

We see gardens with apricot, plum and peach trees. Here are vegetable patches with lettuce and beets. Farmers are working in fields planted with barley and millet. Date palms, fig and pomegranate trees seem to be everywhere.

We now approach the Great City, and cross the deep moat surrounding it. The waters in the moat come from the river Euphrates. Besides the moat, the city is surrounded by a steep wall, brilliantly colored, and wide enough to allow two chariots to be driven abreast on the road which runs along the top of the wall. Babylon is mighty, and its walls extend many miles around.

We choose the gigantic Ishtar gate to enter by, though there are a hundred such gates all delicately engraved in bronze. As we pass through the gateway, the king's guards from the six square towers salute us. The walls of these towers are covered with glazed tile, decorated with a pattern of winged bulls and other fanciful creatures. The Ishtar gate leads us to Procession Avenue, which stretches as far as the eye can see straight through the city. We pass the homes of the wealthy. The bright sun makes the design of enameled drawings of bulls and lions set in the outside walls glisten. We enter through a door, then through a narrow passageway, which leads us to a central courtyard.

Then to the great King Nebuchadnezzar's palace we go, there where Daniel lived and Belshazzar feasted. Its interior, say the Babylonians, is brilliant like the dome of heaven, and its walls decorated like to the splendor of the rising stars.

For Babylon is the mistress of the world. The fleets of Phoenicia sail at its bidding. To Babylon are sent gold and iron from Africa and Spain. The king's mariners, sailing from the Euphrates, bring from India and Ceylon gems, pearls, spices, precious woods. The fleet camels of Arabia bear their precious burdens to this world city.

Fifty broad avenues cross each other, dividing the city into a checkerboard of gigantic squares. That is a convenient way to lay out a city; it is easy to find one's way about. Our friend Nebo, for instance, lives so many blocks north and so many west of the Ishtar gate.

We have wandered to the east side, and we must cross the river Euphrates which flows through the city. Shall we walk over the permanent bridge resting on five stone piers — a wonder in ancient times — or be ferried across in a circular boat, a sort of tub made of leather? Business is centered on the river's many wharves. For the extensive system of canals is the principal means of transportation between the different towns in the kingdom.

The east side of Babylon is the business quarter and the factory district of the city. There women have their beauty shops, and men earn their living as carpenters, cabinetmakers, perfumers, jewelers, metalworkers, and stone-carvers. From beyond the city walls the farmers come here to market their produce.

Babylon is the home of big business. Over on Procession Avenue there is a great clothing factory employing almost two hundred women weavers. Fur, linen, and wool are all used. But for an amazing scene we visit the great temple next to the palace. We seem to be in a modern city hall with all its administrative offices. Here are the tax office, the bureau of weights and measures, and the real estate, recording, and contract departments. Babylon is as well organized as a twentieth-century city.

King Hammurabi, the Great Lawgiver, is responsible for this. "Justice means," thought Hammurabi, "that the weak and poor are protected against the rich and powerful." So he established laws for wages and rent, for making businessmen responsible for their contracts, for helping the farmer. Among the great lawgivers of the world, Hammurabi the Babylonian stands high.

Yonder is a fellow, clad in the tunic and sandals of the day, who is strangely busy. In one hand he holds a slab of damp clay, like a biscuit; in the other, a stylus, a piece of reed, which he presses on the soft clay. The sharp jabs of the stylus leave wedge-shaped or nail-like marks on the clay. The clay tablet is then left to dry. To make sure that the clay tablet will not crumble, the scribe may then bake it in an oven. The clay tablet will shrivel in size, but it will also become a hard brick, which can last for thousands of years. It can only be destroyed by being crushed into small pieces. The lump of clay is a letter, and its envelope a thin clay covering on which the scribe writes the address and then stamps his seal on it.

The scribe is an important personage in Babylon, the most highly educated man there. He has been to school; he has learned reading, writing, arithmetic, and grammar. Any Babylonian who wishes to communicate with a friend, say in Nineveh or Sumer, must ask the scribe to write for him.

"The king has commanded me," says the scribe proudly, "to translate one of our great poems on the rock outside the city." He recites part of the poem for us:

> *When the young dawn gleamed forth,*
> *From the foundations of heaven a black*
> *cloud arose . . .*

We go on. Everywhere in Babylon we see wonders. Within the city walls are enormous temples with bronze doors, courts of justice, royal libraries lined with clay books, an astronomical observatory, and the famed hanging gardens. And everywhere — whether in Babylon, or Nineveh, or Persepolis — we see the cuneiform tablets on which the scholars are writing their history, their medicine, and their astronomy.

IV

Our knowledge of this long-dead world — our ability to read these ancient tablets — we owe especially to such scholars as Henry Creswicke Rawlinson. Every bygone age leaves its tracks in the dust of time, where those who explore ancient life — the archaeologists — read the story of the ages. Their work is somewhat like rummaging in the attic for clues of grandfather's past life. To an archaeologist a piece of clay, a sliver of wood, or a trinket may be eloquent, and our understanding of ancient history depends on men like Rawlinson, who explored not only foreign lands but past ages. For instance, some scholars used to scoff at the legend of Troy. "Troy never existed," they said. "It was only imagined by Homer."

In 1829 Heinrich Schliemann, a little German boy, was very much troubled by this disbelief. He liked Homer. He liked to hear his father tell the story about the ancient Greek heroes fighting at the walls of Troy. "Father, was there really such a town as Troy?" Heinrich would ask.

"Perhaps," his father explained, "but even if Troy once existed, nothing remains of it."

Then, one day, the father gave his eight-year-old boy a history book which had a drawing showing a few Trojans escaping the conquered city, which was in flames. "Father," he cried, "did Troy have such huge walls as in this picture?"

"It probably did."

"I say that if it had such thick walls, some ruins must still remain beneath the dust. Some day," he vowed, "I shall uncover them."

When Heinrich Schliemann grew up he went to the Dardanelles, where he thought Troy once stood. There he began to dig for the ancient capital of King Priam. Bit by bit the walls of a fortified town began to be disclosed, and within a short time three great gates were uncovered. The roadway of the largest of these passed through a huge tower. To Schliemann it seemed that this was "the great tower of Ilios" guarding the Skaian Gates, where Helen anxiously watched the duel between Menelaus and Paris. Schliemann continued his excavations. Under the top layer of ruins he found the remains of a still earlier settlement. By the time he finished his dig he had revealed a Troy far older than the Homeric one. For the ruins of nine cities are piled one on top of the other. One of them was Homer's Troy.

"Since Homer told the truth about the town of Troy," Schliemann announced, "then the rest of the Iliad must be true. For instance, King Agamemnon, the leader of the Greeks, was ruler of Mycenae, on the Greek mainland. Surely there must be some relics of his palace, or at least of the town of Mycenae."

"Troy," Greek scholars conceded, "did exist. But that does not mean that the rest of the Iliad is true. You will soon be telling us that there really was a Nestor, whose palace was in an ancient town called Pylos, and that the Greek warriors were clad in bronze armor. Homer told a fanciful tale. Remember, the Greek warriors in those days were primitive people. Greek writing had not yet been invented. How could Homer recite about kings who lived centuries before he did?"

Heinrich Schliemann disregarded such talk. In that desolate region of Greece, he found the royal tombs of Mycenae, and excavated a treasure trove of bronze armor, gold-inlaid swords, golden goblets, and hundreds of ornaments and artistic vases. Schliemann had uncovered a civilization that flourished more than five hundred years before Homer, and that had cities, palaces, art and a form of Greek writing.

Henry Rawlinson and Heinrich Schliemann had unlocked ancient civilizations that mankind had forgotten.

Richard Francis Burton

(1821–1890)

"THE THOUSAND NIGHTS AND A NIGHT"

I

Not long ago — in 1850 — there was a huge white blot on the map, called Arabia. What the blot hid was a mystery. Who dwelt within it, what the face of the land, were dark secrets. Now and then a caravan of Moslem pilgrims would march out of Yambu on the Red Sea and fade into the desert. And the desert was silent.

Somewhere in that huge blot were the sacred cities of Medina and Mecca. Entrance within their gates was forbidden to any but a Moslem. No others dared to enter for fear of inviting death. About these cities lay the desert, parched and swarming with robber bands.

Mr. Charles Cole, the English Consul at Jedda on the Red Sea, wrote home that he had spoken with many Mohammedans on the subject of exploring unknown Arabia, and clearing up the huge blot on our maps. The Moslems merely shook their heads at such talk.

"We English can do it," Mr. Cole cried rashly.

His hearers shrugged. An Englishman could do a

great many things, they agreed. But he could never enter Medina or Mecca. He would die in the attempt. If the desert did not exhaust him completely, the brigands, lurking in the hills of the desert, would slay him. Lastly, if he were lucky enough to escape these deaths, he would be torn to pieces within the cities . . . No, no, let the huge white blot be.

One of Mr. Cole's countrymen, Richard Burton, was a young scholar and adventurer. For ten years or more he had studied Eastern peoples, their manners, customs, and languages. He spoke twenty-nine different Oriental languages so well that if he were properly disguised he could pass for a native almost anywhere in the Orient.

Burton saw the blot on the map.

"Shameful!" he exclaimed, as he vowed to clear it up.

II

On April 4, 1853, a young Persian prince — at least he looked like a prince and said he was one — embarked on the steamer *Bengal* sailing to Alexandria from Southampton, England. The prince was tall, his cheekbones prominent, his complexion swarthy, and his mustachios envied by all very young Englishmen. The prince himself spoke no English, and since no one on board spoke Persian, he remained a silent prince for the entire voyage.

The ship no sooner docked at Alexandria than the

prince hurried away, and anyone following him through the twisted streets would certainly have been struck by a queer thing: one day the prince entered his lodgings never to issue forth again. Instead, a dervish, a wanderer of the desert, stole out of the prince's lodgings carrying some baggage on his shoulder. He was tall, with prominent cheekbones, and flowing mustachios.

At the docks Moslem pilgrims to the holy cities were waiting for a boat to take them first to Cairo. They noticed the dervish.

"What is your name, O Father of the Mustachios?" they asked him.

"Abdullah," was the reply. "I am an Afghan."

Up the Nile to Cairo the pilgrims sailed. Then, in a body, they trudged across to Suez. At Suez they were packed into a small boat which, amid creakings and shoutings, set out on the Red Sea for Yambu on the Arabian coast. The dervish Abdullah was a silent figure, except when addressed. At first the rest of the pilgrims were a bit suspicious of him, but when they heard his wise words, they began to like him.

"A sage and holy man," they whispered.

When the pilgrim ship had been several days out at sea, it was anchored one night close to the shore. At dawn, the pilgrims found that the tide had ebbed and the boat was stranded. There was nothing to do but shove the boat out into the water. Shove they did, but all their efforts were of no avail. All the morning they pushed and strained in vain. The dervish stood off, watching their frantic efforts. Suddenly he noticed the tide flowing in and the vessel yielding. Cunningly he approached the heaving mob.

"When you hear me pronounce my words," he said, "heave with all your might."

Raising his hands, he chanted: *"Ya Piran Pir! Ya abd al-Kadir Jilani!"*

The mob strained, the boat dipped, a wave lifted it, and once more it floated on the tide.

"A miracle!" said the pilgrims in awed tones.

At Yambu the ragged pilgrims formed a caravan, and with their camels and dromedaries stepped forth into the desert. Across this lay Medina. Oh, the terrible desert! That sea of sand! The sky is a pitiless blinding glare. The mouth glows; the skin is parched. The sky raises up pillars of sand which, like jinn of the waste, advance toward you monstrously. The Arab stretches out his finger at these jinn and exclaims defiantly, "O thou ill-omened ones!" The simoon, poison wind, breathes on the cheek like the flaming breath of a tiger.

The little caravan was approached by brigands several times. Each time, however, it succeeded in squirming its way onward. The dervish earned a curious reputation in these encounters. When the pilgrims reached Medina, they said to the natives, pointing to the Father of the Mustachios, "Do you know what he did?"

"No."

"Well, the other day some robbers surrounded us out there. They showed us death, and what do you think he did?"

"How do we know! What *did* he do?"

"He called for his dinner."

That was enough to endear him permanently to the Arab's heart, for the desert loves a brave man. But the people of the holy city would not have been so cordial to the dervish perhaps, had they seen him secretly writing his mysterious notes and drawings. In the dead of night, or whenever he was alone, the Father of the Mustachios was constantly writing and hiding away his papers. Fortunately, his hosts loved him too much to suspect him.

With tears and presents they said farewell to him at last, when he left Medina for the sacred Mecca.

Again the perils of the desert, the bullets of brigands! But the dervish was silent and unafraid, and continued to call loudly for his supper. "In my country, Afghanistan," said he, "we mind not the jackal of the desert."

"Thou hast spoken truth, O gracious one," said his listeners.

Safely therefore to Mecca came the dervish. The city was like a vast Moslem bazaar. The pavements were filled with a motley crowd. Here a Bedouin, there a Hindu, yonder a Turk. And over all towered the minarets of Mecca. The dervish drank it all in. His pencil scrawled secretly.

Abdullah stepped into the office of the British Consulate in Jedda. The servant, contemptuous of the Afghan, did not think that Mr. Cole could see him. The dervish held out a note. Humbly he beseeched that Mr. Cole be given the note.

In a short while the astonished servant returned to

say that Mr. Cole would see Abdullah in the private
office. Abdullah quietly followed into the presence of
Mr. Cole.

"Richard Burton!" cried the consul.

The dervish nodded wearily.

III

Back in England, Burton was no sooner up from the
task of writing his *Personal Narrative of a Pilgrimage
to Al Medinah and Meccah,* than he looked about for a
new adventure. As a knight in quest of danger, he
could not bear the tame life of London. Dress dinners
in his honor and polite speeches bored him.

"Oh for the solitude of the wild place, the peace of
the desert, the excitement of the strange face, the sound
of a strange tongue!" he wished.

The Royal Geographical Society came to his rescue.
"There are hints," said the scholars, "of a busy life in
East Africa, the part called Somaliland. Who are its
people, what lives and what grows in its plains and in
its forests? We hear of an ancient walled city in its interior, Harar by name, once the capital of a mighty race.
It seems to be the headquarters of the slave trade and
the coffee trade. But that is only hearsay. The slaves,
who are shipped to the coast from out of its dark walls
at less than a dollar a head, speak of a strange language
and of an emir who forbids all strangers entrance to his
city. You, dear Burton, so expert in clearing up blots
on the map, are the one man for this task. No European
has ever been there, and our government will not pro-

tect you. Will you take your life again into your hands?"

As fast as he could Burton went to Arabia. In the British colony of Aden, on the southern coast of Arabia, he made his preparations.

"To Harar?" exclaimed his friends in Aden. "Horror, indeed. It is a forbidden city surrounded by desert plains. There is a limit to rashness. Even you will not escape death."

Such talk only added zest to the adventure. Burton disguised himself as an Arab merchant this time, at the head of a caravan of horses, mules, and camels. Then with his troop, as his friends threw the slipper of good luck at his back, he boarded a boat to Zayla, the outpost of Somaliland on the east coast of Africa.

On the bright clear tide, the Arab servants of Burton showed themselves true sons of the open. They doffed their clothes and smeared their bodies with fat. Under the moonlight they rested on mats, smoking their pipes made out of the goat's shank bone. They slept on deck and there gobbled food, wiping their greasy fingers on their ankles.

Among the whitewashed houses and yellow sands of Zayla, Burton found a curious mixture of people. In color they ranged from jet black to olive.

"They are all kind to me," wrote Burton in his notebook, "but the Negroes especially are merry, soft, and affectionate. They delight in dancing, and sing to the accompaniment of the drum and the clapping of hands. The poetry of their songs is very good, for the people are all poets here. Everybody has a fine ear for rhythm.

And they take poetry so seriously that a bad rhyme makes them indignant."

For twenty-six days Burton stayed in Zayla, days of conversation over coffee and pipes. He studied their weapons and took as great a delight as the natives in practicing with long thin spears and throwing eighteen-inch daggers at a target. Burton soon acquired the reputation of being the strongest man in Zayla.

As he wandered outside the low brown wall of the town, he came upon tents of the Bedouins, the Sun-dwellers, as the Arabs called these riders of the plains who brought to Zayla the products of the desert.

To mingle with the Bedouins, a generous and hospitable people, was Burton's delight. After a supper of rice and dates, he would read to an attentive audience tales from the *Arabian Nights*. Or they would talk. Talk was life to them. Suppose a Bedouin rides forth to the well for water. When he comes back, he meets a few companions. If they should ask him "What's the news?" the conversation would go like this, Burton said.

> "It is good news."
> "Even so," his hearers nod.
> "I mounted mule this morning."
> "Even so!"
> "I departed from you riding."
> "Even so!"
> "*There* I went."
> "Even so!"
> "I threaded the wood."
> "Even so!"
> "I traversed the sands."
> "Even so!"
> "At last I came upon cattle tracks."

"Hoo! Hoo! Hoo!"
"They were fresh."
"Even so!"
"So were the earths."
"Even so!"
"I distinguished the feet of women."
"Even so!"
"But there were no camels."
"Even so!"
"At last I saw sticks . . ."
"Even so!"
"Stones . . ."
"Even so!"
"Water . . ."
"Even so!"
"A well!"

One night, as they were enjoying the cool breeze after the steam of the day, a rider came in to announce that the road to Harar was closed; a dead man had been found on the way, and smallpox was raging on the plains that stretched between Zayla and Harar.

"Now you must stay with us," said the Bedouins triumphantly to Burton. "You cannot go on."

Burton smiled.

"But surely you will not," cried his servants. "We will not go. Life is too dear."

The "merchant" shrugged his shoulders. "I will go alone, if necessary," he said.

"Woe!" they moaned. "We are dead men."

Before them rose the wooded mountains, purple and silver in the moonlight. From the mysterious depths the hyena howled its laugh, and the breeze carried the unearthly shriek of the jackal.

IV

The "merchant" carried bales of sheeting, canvas, watches, tobacco, beads, earrings and other trinkets. The way to Harar lay sometimes on the open plain and sometimes in the gloom of a forest. And the plain was sometimes made pleasant by cool wells and freshets banked with the green graceful tamarisk, the thick jujube, or the gum-giving acacia. By moonlight the wells were haunted by strange forms. Now a troop of gazelles stepped daintily up to drink; now the lumbering elephant. The shadow was that of a lion pacing about, or of an ostrich strutting, or perhaps of a snake streaking the sand with its trail. Sometimes it was the most fearful of monsters, the leopard, who has been known to follow a file of travelers in the wood, with stealthy tread, leap out and strike down the last man and drag him away to his lair.

At the head of the little band rode Burton, his rifle cocked across his saddle. All went well until from a hill they saw a dark speck far off in the yellow stubble.

"Harar!" he shouted.

His men became cold with fright. "Turn back!" they beseeched.

"He who desires may desert me," said Burton. "I go on."

They took him at his word, and all but two turned back.

Boldly Burton entered the gates of Harar. "I desire audience with the emir," he demanded loudly. He objected when they commanded him to take off his shoes in the palace. He objected when they asked him to leave his revolver behind. He objected and bullied. And his bullying took effect. The men of Harar were cowed.

The emir, Sultan Ahmad bin Sultan Abibakr, sat in a dark room on a raised cot. Around him ranged his court.

"Peace be upon ye!" saluted Burton.

He threw off his disguise. "I am a European," he announced boldly.

Narrowly he watched the emir. If he smiled, all was well. If not . . . The emir was frowning.

"I have come from Aden to bring to you the compliments of our governor," Burton went on in Arabic. The emir's brow was dark.

"I have come to Harar to gaze on the light of Your Majesty's countenance."

His Majesty was silent.

"I convey to you our governor's wish that our two nations may learn the ways of peace and friendship."

The emir smiled, and his smile was like the light of the sun to Burton.

That night, as he lay down on the hard matting in the emir's house, Burton, too, smiled a contented smile.

V

The world has never boasted a more adventurous soul than the scholar Richard Burton. Wherever an unexplored spot of the world appeared on our maps, he was restless to invade and clear it. And always among the strange people of his faraway adventures, he care-

fully studied their speech and habits and way of living.
Thus he learned to speak in twenty-nine different
tongues — almost as flawlessly as he spoke and wrote
English.

For years at a time Europe lost sight of Burton. Then
suddenly one day he would appear in Europe from
lands of mystery, haggard with suffering. And as he
rested awhile, he wrote down his adventures, his new
facts about geography and the life of hidden tribes of
people.

After the *First Footsteps in East Africa* came the
brave journey which resulted in Burton's greatest discovery. Scholars had long wondered, "What are the
sources of the Nile?" Everybody else guessed and did
nothing more, but Burton thought grimly, "The Nile
must be tracked down." He packed up, and off he went.
Along with him went his friend John Hanning Speke.
Down into Central Africa the two explorers tracked the
great river, and in February, 1858, they found themselves in a region of lakes. Here Burton discovered the
immense sheet of water known as Lake Tanganyika;
and Speke, while Burton lay sick, discovered Lake Victoria Nyanza, the source of the Nile. The book which
Burton wrote celebrating the discovery is *The Lake
Regions of Equatorial Africa.*

All his life Burton continued his explorations: again
in Africa, in the western United States, in Iceland. To
record all his adventures he had to write about eighty
books.

Then, as a scholar, he made the most delightful
translation into English of the *Arabian Nights,* called
The Thousand Nights and a Night, and the best trans-

lation of the Portuguese Camoëns' "Lusiads," a poem about another great adventurer, Vasco da Gama.

Well has it been said that Richard Burton crowded more adventure and study into one lifetime than is usual in ten.

David Livingstone

(1813–1873)

INSIDE AFRICA

I

AT THE AGE of ten, when he should have been romping about in the sunshine, David was already leading the life of a responsible adult. He dressed by candlelight and hurried in the gray chill morning, not to school or playground, but to a cotton factory in the town of Blantyre, Scotland. That was his school. Perched on a ledge of his spinning jenny was the Latin grammar he had bought with his first few shillings.

"Hic, haec, hoc," he muttered while the machine whirred and the air thickened with cotton shreds.

At eight in the evening he shut the book and dashed off to night school. The subject that fascinated him was geography. It was the magic carpet upon which he floated to the ends of the earth and back again . . . by ten o'clock. Up to that time he could alight on the steppes of Asia or climb on the back of a llama in Peru, just as he liked. The world of geography was his playground.

Except for Africa. On its map was the annoying expression: Unexplored. Africa, in 1825, was mostly that.

The fringe of settlements on its coasts was only an edge of light around a dark pool from which rose vaporous legends of pygmies and unicorns and terrible evils. Not that there hadn't been explorers brave enough to confront the evils. They had indeed ventured into the interior of Africa. Only, they had never come back. Africa was known as the white man's grave.

Unexplored. To David the word was a door shut in his face, like the door he shut when he scrubbed his mother's floor because he didn't care to be seen doing a girl's work.

He had an inspiration: if he went to the unexplored place it would be unexplored no longer. People lived there and he would meet them. And if they didn't know geography or Latin, why, he would teach them. He would help them in all ways, as he helped his mother. He could be a missionary and help them in the conduct of their lives. If they were sick he could make them well. But, then of course, he would have to be a doctor . . . It was ten o'clock, time to stop dreaming. He still had his homework to do before midnight.

II

"Where are you going?" a native chieftain had exclaimed as Dr. Livingstone prepared to explore the Kalahari Desert. "You will surely die of sun and thirst."

At that time he had been in search of Lake Ngami, which everyone had heard of but no white man had seen. He had found it and the discovery brought him fame.

Now in the summer of 1852 he was attempting something of far greater importance to the people of Africa and the world at large. From time immemorial the millions of people in the interior of Africa had been organized into tribes, each one segregated from the others. Each tribe feared its neighbor on the far side of the forest or the opposite bank of the river.

"If," thought Livingstone, "roads were laid down and communication made easy their mutual fears might end. And if a route could be mapped across the continent, then the people of Africa and people of other lands could meet, trade goods and ideas, and everyone would be richer and wiser." Most importantly, the civilized public would have its attention called to the vile trade in human beings, the slave trade, and horrified, they would put a stop to it.

Such was David Livingstone's hope as he led his Bushmen porters and his ox-drawn wagons north from Capetown. He was in the prime of life, a powerful man with a shock of hair and a trimmed mustache. He had a determined jaw and steady gaze.

The caravan moved into lovely country. Often the grass topped the wagons. They passed huge banyans, as the wild fig tree was called. By day herds of elands watched them pass, unaware of being within range of guns. Around the campfire a line of buffaloes filed past just as fearlessly. A lion roared and was answered.

They came to Zulu country, to the village of Linyanti, to the Makololo tribe. Its chief, Sekeletu, was only eighteen years old. He had inherited the title from his father who had just died. A herald greeted Livingstone, chanting: "Don't I see the white man? Don't I see the father of Sekeletu?" Gifts were exchanged ceremoniously — Sekeletu offering an ox, milk and beer; Livingstone reciprocating with yards of cloth and strings of beads.

Now to celebrate the arrival of a white friend the people danced and sang. The men arranged themselves in a circle, everyone shouting hilariously. In unison they drummed out a rhythm by stamping twice with one leg and once with the other as they tossed their heads and arms about. Outside the circle the women beat time with handclaps.

Livingstone had taken care to learn something of their speech and he told them his purpose as an explorer, his vision of peace and dignity for Africans. Sekeletu said that in so glorious an undertaking he would like to help. He ordered a number of his men to go along with Dr. Livingstone who promised to bring them back safe.

The enlarged caravan pushed north and then west. The forest grew more dense and gloomy. The dreadful evils of Africa now came out to meet them: the tsetse fly and dysentery. The first killed almost all the oxen; the second infected Livingstone. From that day on fever never left him. Day by day it sapped his strength. In his flesh he felt the saying: Africa, the white man's grave. But the thought of going back never occurred to him.

They came to the domain of the Chiboque and Livingstone sent customary gifts to their chief, Njambi. But to his dismay instead of return gifts, Njambi sent back a scornful message demanding more. As tribute he demanded two things: a man and a gun. Indignant, Livingstone replied that he was no slave dealer. The chief's answer was to mobilize a force and with drawn

swords to surround the camp. Livingstone's men met
them with javelins at the ready and the two opposed
forces stood on the point of mutual slaughter.

Livingstone sat on a camp stool, double-barreled gun
across his knees. He looked straight at Njambi.

"Sit down."

His resolute manner made the invitation a command. The chief sat down.

"What is our crime for which you come to attack
us?"

Njambi began to storm. The gift had been a measly
one, he shouted. Moreover, the man who brought the
gift had deliberately spat upon one of his men. (This
was untrue.) "I, Njambi, therefore fine you one man."

"I have no right to give you one of my men," said
Livingstone. "We are all free men."

The chief thought this ridiculous, but seeing that the
white man was adamant, he said: "Well, at least give
me a gun."

"Not that, either. You would want to use it upon us."

"I demand payment for your passage through my
land."

"This is God's land, not yours."

Suddenly one of Njambi's men charged at Livingstone from behind. Just as swiftly Livingstone swung
around the muzzle of his gun and the man stepped
back. At the same time Livingstone's men surrounded
Njambi.

"We want only to be permitted to go in peace," said
Livingstone. "You want to fight. Very well. We will
wait for you to strike the first blow."

The blow was not struck and the caravan moved on.

Throughout his long trek to the coast, the longest in African exploration up to his time, Livingstone often met chiefs like Njambi but just as often friendly ones like Sekeletu. With the Njambis he always tried patient reasoning. If that didn't work he drew his pistol. So the caravan after much hardship reached the west coast at Loanda in Angola. Livingstone was very sick and his men were exhausted.

"But, my dear fellow," protested the British consul, "you can't go on in your condition. You must go back home and recover your health. Let me arrange for your passage on the very first boat."

Livingstone wouldn't hear of it. He had promised to bring his Makololo men safely back to their tribe. Besides, he hadn't finished the job of finding the transcontinental route. From Capetown he had gone up the center and turned west at Linyanti. Now he had to retrace his steps to Linyanti and continue east clear to the Indian Ocean. He rested awhile and then took to the road again.

"Don't I see the white man, the father of Sekeletu? Don't I see our brothers come back to us?" Again the herald intoned his welcome.

At the sight of Livingstone's wasted frame the young chief was deeply moved. He too urged his white friend not to go on, but since Livingstone was determined, the chief accompanied him with his force of more than a hundred men. The first night out, there was a fall of heavy rain. The bare ground was their bed. Livingstone had no blanket and he lay down, shivering. He heard a footfall and opened his eyes to see the young chief gently lay his own blanket over him.

Their progress was slow because they had to avoid traveling through the rain forest, lair of the dreaded tsetse. When they were forced to traverse the forest they did so by night, for the tsetse bites only by day.

But progress they made, and one day Livingstone pushed aside some shrubs and there before his eyes rolled the majestic waters of the Zambezi River. Feathery palm stood against the sky, silver beeches and dark cypresses. Over all towered the burly baobab. The explorers launched canoes and after some days beheld the most breathtaking sight of all Livingstone's days.

"Look!"

In the distance five columns of vapor were rising high in the air. A deep roar sounded. "The Smoke-That-Sounds," Sekeletu said in a tone of awe.

Livingstone crept to the verge of the falls where, peering down, he saw the Zambezi, a thousand yards broad, leap down a precipice and rush on, boiling, through a canyon hundreds of feet in depth. Dense white clouds rose from the tumbling river. Livingstone looked up. Within the clouds shone two rainbows.

"Let us," he proposed, "call these falls after the queen of my country. Victoria Falls."

No route was established. The geographical results were as related: giving place names here and there. His great contribution was humanitarian.

III

Now ravaged by fever, he took passage back to England. To his embarrassment he found himself famous. The Royal Geographical Society conferred its medal of honor upon him. The Queen gave him audience. He was in demand as lecturer. Dr. Livingstone was a modest man. But he was dedicated to help the people of Africa. So he overcame his embarrassment and told their story as he knew it.

With the change of climate his health improved and he was able to write his first of several books of travels. He told of the friendly races of Africa: Bushmen, Hottentots, Zulus. He told how as a doctor he tried to relieve their suffering, how he taught them to increase their crops by digging a network of ditches to draw water from a distant stream. He wrote of quiet mornings in bright meadows, of the picture of women coming up from the river with watering pots poised on their heads. He wrote of the birds and beasts, of francolins and koodoos and elands. Throughout his speeches and his writing he kept hammering at the slave trade until he stirred the conscience of his audience. Young men especially were fired with enthusiasm. Many of them prepared to go and do as he did.

He himself went back to Africa as soon as he was able, this time as leader of an official British expedition.

One day while he and his party were exploring the Zambezi valley he happened to witness a scene which changed him from an explorer to a crusader. The territory they were in had been subjugated by the Portugese some three centuries before, and was considered a colony of Portugal. Livingstone had heard that the Portugese were vicious slavers. That morning he saw the evidence. As he was rounding a hill he came suddenly upon a long line of manacled men, women and children. They were being whipped on by guards armed with muskets. Livingstone was a British official and a guest of the Portugese government, but without regard for consequences he took matters into his own hands. He drove off the guards and cut the chains of the captives. All of them fell on their knees before their liberators. Many were mere children. One small boy said: "The other white man tied and starved us. You cut our chains and tell us to eat. Why are you different?" One woman said that her infant had been killed before her eyes because she could not carry both her load and her baby. A man was axed to death because he had broken down with fatigue. A favorite trick to round up slaves, Livingstone was told, was to set fire to a village and seize the homeless.

As soon as he had the leisure he wrote a book exposing the slave trade in all its horror. He called the slave trade the open running sore of the world. "Stop it," he urged. "Use force."

IV

The eyes of the world were now upon David Livingstone, following all his moves. He announced the discovery of Lake Nyasa. He explored the valley of the Shire. He discovered Lake Moero. The following year he discovered Lake Bangweulu. He was creating the geography of Africa, putting lights into the dark continent. Outside of Africa people read about the discoveries in their morning newspapers. Africa and Dr. Livingstone became favorite table talk. Then suddenly he disappeared from view. His mailing address had been simply: Dr. Livingstone, Africa. A letter so addressed was delivered in Capetown, passed from hand to hand, from tribe to tribe. A Makololo carried it to a Bechuana (whom the Makololo distrusted). The Bechuana carried it to a Zulu (whom he feared). Eventually the letter reached Dr. Livingstone. But now in the fall of 1869 he was not to be found. The public was deeply concerned. Was he alive?

He was barely alive.

In the village of Ujiji near Lake Tanganyika he lay in a grass hut racking his weary brains. How could he persuade the Arabs who ruled the region to give up slavery? As he brooded over the problem his servant rushed in with the news that a caravan had arrived, headed by a white man. The white man was asking for him. Livingstone stepped outside. The caravan was flaunting the Stars and Stripes.

The leader approached. He raised his hat. "Dr. Livingstone, I presume," he said. "I am Henry Stanley of the New York *Herald*. I have been sent to find you."

In the depths of the jungle, where New York and London were unknown except to the two white men, they clasped hands and the reporter got his story. Dr. Livingstone concluded: "On this great land men are hunted like wild beasts, and I ask: what is the civilized world going to do about it? Will you take that message back with you?"

"I will," said Stanley. "But Doctor, you are not well. You must go back to England at once."

"Not yet. There is still work for me here."

He had brought light into what was once the dark continent. He had mapped more of it than anyone before or since his time. But, yes, much more remained to

be done if Africa was to be free. He could not foresee
that his death, not far off, would mobilize world opinion so strongly that slavery would be stamped out in
short order.

For David Livingstone had set Africans on the path
of history, where they could not avoid meeting other
nations. The French would come, the English, the
Dutch, the Belgians. Other nations, too. They would
parcel out the primitive continent and its people for
themselves. They would send their colonists, their engineers and bankers. They would develop the wealth of
the land. The people of Africa would learn from them.
Then one fine day Africans would insist on being on
their own, independent of their teachers.

David Livingstone could not foresee that freedom
and independence would one day come to the many nations of Africa. That his people, as he called the Africans, would one day contribute greatly to the material
wealth of the world, of that he was certain. He could
not, however, imagine the spiritual debt that the world
would owe "his people." For African art, its beautiful
sculpture especially, and African folk music have
greatly influenced world culture.

"But you must go home, Doctor," Stanley kept repeating.

He did. To his final home. It happened in a grass hut
on May 1, 1873.

Roald Amundsen

(1872–1928)

FINDING THE NORTHWEST PASSAGE

I

HENRY HUDSON lost his life seeking the Northwest Passage. Before him, John and Sebastian Cabot spent a good part of their lives seeking it in vain. And that most successful of explorers, Captain Cook, was baffled by it.

Although he knew this, Sir John Franklin in 1819 did not hesitate. For the English government said, "Somewhere to the north, between Newfoundland and Greenland, must be a direct passage to the East. If you find it, twenty thousand pounds and immortal fame are yours."

"I shall try," said Franklin, "and if I die in the attempt to further man's knowledge, it will be in the company of brave men."

He sailed through the treacherous passes of northern Canada, through blizzard and fog. Then, in weather so cold that the mercury in the thermometers froze and tea in their teapots became ice before they could drink it, Franklin and four companions set out on the land.

To protect themselves against the weather, the men

wore fur caps, leather coats and trousers, heavy stockings and moccasins. They traveled on snowshoes, which, although necessary for snow-covered ground, meant much suffering for those unaccustomed to walking on them. To carry their supplies they used two sledges, made of a few flat boards, curving upward in front, and drawn by dogs.

They had to live by their daily hunting and fishing. For five weeks they wandered slowly across stretches of barren land and over high and rugged hills, each man carrying one hundred eighty pounds of supplies, including a canoe. On the icy waters of the river that led to the Arctic, they found themselves hurled down the stream, over rocks which would have wrecked the helpless canoes, had they struck the jagged edges. Then along the rockbound coast of the Arctic their canoes tossed in a tempestuous sea.

Franklin surveyed the coast line. "A Northwest Passage to China exists, and we shall sail through it," he said.

Overcome by fatigue and weakened from lack of food, they struggled on. A violent storm arose. The men shivered under their blankets in their frozen tents, about which the snow was piled. The food supply was low, and the long Arctic winter had returned. For days a violent storm of wind and rain beat on them. Franklin retreated.

"We had no means of making a fire," he wrote in his journal, "the moss being covered by the ice and snow. On being exposed to the air, I became quite faint with hunger. . . . We commenced our cheerless march. The ground was covered with snow a foot in depth, and

we had to pass across swamps and marshy places, sometimes stepping up to the knee in water, and at others on
a slippery stone which often brought us down. The
men who carried the canoes had a most laborious task.
They frequently fell down. The best canoe was so damaged as to be rendered wholly useless."

II

Near the town of Oslo, in Norway, a fifteen-year-old
boy was so thrilled by the book he was reading that he
did not hear his mother calling him to supper. The
book was Sir John Franklin's account of his polar journey.

"For three hundred years the bravest English explorers have tried to go through the Northwest Passage and
failed," the boy said to himself. "The bravest of all was
Sir John Franklin and he, too, died in the attempt. But
that Northwest Passage must be conquered. For whatever remains a mystery is a burden to all men. I shall
solve the mystery of the Northwest Passage."

From then on, Roald Amundsen began to prepare
for the life of an Arctic explorer. This meant that he
must train himself to endure every hardship. The only
sports then in Norway were skiing and football. Roald
liked to ski, but he did not like football. Nevertheless,
since it hardened his muscles, he played the game as
enthusiastically as the greatest lover of that sport.

Meanwhile he was devouring all the books on the
Arctic regions he could lay his hands on.

"Why hasn't man been able to conquer the Northwest Passage these three hundred years?" he wondered.

"Since Sebastian Cabot and Henry Hudson thought of reaching Asia by sailing west over the northern route, generations of hardy Arctic explorers have steered their ships that way. Always barriers of ice blocked them. Yet they were the bravest of pioneers. Why did they fail?"

Amundsen found out. There was the long Arctic night, which meant months and months of patiently waiting in the dreary wastes of ice and snow, with frightful winter cold and piercing winds, and darkness relieved only by the moon and the northern lights. He read of ships frozen in between great walls of ice that held them prisoner until spring set them free. For the ship's crew this meant scurvy and hunger, if they were fortunate enough to survive the Arctic winter. When the sun finally broke up the surrounding ice, there were only a few short weeks left of summer to go forward or back. But often the warmth of the Arctic summer was not sufficient to clear the channel. At the end of the season, the explorers would then find their ship imprisoned in the ice a few miles from their previous winter quarters, short of food.

"These explorers were certainly courageous," Amundsen decided. "But we need something more than bravery. We must plan ahead and prepare every detail in our expeditions. That is how we can conquer the Northwest Passage."

Thereupon he began training himself all the harder. For instance, he studied navigation. So good a student was he that by the time he was twenty-five, he was chosen first mate on the *Belgica*, which was sailing for the Antarctic to study the South Magnetic Pole. On the way, the boat coasted along Tierra del Fuego, where the commander gathered specimens, mapped the coast line, and took meteorological observations.

Now a bitter experience awaited the young explorer. As the expedition proceeded to South Victoria Land, they were caught in an ice field. For thirteen months the ship was frozen in. Two of the sailors went insane. To add to the misery, at one time everyone on board ship was affected with scurvy.

From his reading Amundsen knew that scurvy could be cured by a change of diet. The only fresh food obtainable was fresh meat. To get that meant traveling for miles over ice in search of seals and penguins. But he brought back the cure. Within a week the health of the crew improved.

When he returned to Europe, Amundsen equipped himself further by studying magnetism and meteorology, for he wished his explorations to be of value to the world. He therefore went to see George Von Neumayer, a German scientist, about his studies.

The scientist greeted Amundsen and asked him his business. Amundsen explained that he wanted to be an explorer, that he had had two years' experience with an Antarctic expedition, and that he must learn more about making magnetic observations.

"Young man," replied the aged scientist, "you have something else on your mind! Tell me what it is."

"I want to be the first to conquer the Northwest Passage."

"Ah, a fine ambition. There is still more."

"Well," said Amundsen, "I have wanted to locate exactly the North Magnetic Pole."

The scientist arose, came over to Amundsen, and threw his arms around him in a warm embrace. "Young man," he said, "if you do that, you will be the benefactor of mankind for ages to come. *That* is the great adventure."

During the night of June 16, 1903, in the midst of a blinding rainstorm, seven men boarded the fishing smack *Gjöa*, tied to a wharf on the coast of Norway. The hawsers cast off, the prow of the *Gjöa* turned to the great adventure.

For days the *Gjöa* cut quietly through the waters until Amundsen reached the islands north of Canada. Here Amundsen took magnetic observations to locate the North Magnetic Pole. The observations showed it to be on the west coast of Boothia Peninsula.

They entered Peel Sound.

"From here on," Captain Amundsen told his gallant crew of six, "nobody has ever ventured. We have no charts to go by. We must therefore constantly take soundings, and make our own maps as we proceed. Anything may happen to us."

Everything happened. A mad gale seized them and frisked them as a child does a penny toy. On one side the sea heaved them to a dizzy height; on the other it yawned and showed jagged rocks, like teeth in a vast grinning skull. Crash! The keel ground on the rocks. It seemed all over with the brave *Gjöa*. But no! Another swell, like a mountain, swept the boat off the rocks.

The men rushed out to search for a leak.

"We are saved," they cried joyfully. "There is no leak."

Suddenly the helmsman groaned, "Captain, the rudder is damaged. We are drifting helplessly."

The men shuddered. All at once a wall of water sent them sprawling. As they struggled to hold on a little longer for dear life, the helmsman shrieked, "She steers! She steers again!"

The wave had knocked the rudder back into place! They were safe for a little while longer. But they clung to life so firmly that neither sea nor rocks nor the Arctic ice could down them.

September found them cruising in Rae Strait. The Arctic night was drawing on, and it was time to set up winter quarters. As he scanned the horizon, Amundsen spied King William Land and a beautiful sheltered harbor, safe from storms. Here the explorers built a snug camp for themselves, and kennels for their dogs.

Their boxes were now taken ashore and unpacked. The cases were made of boards cut from the most carefully selected lumber. They could use them in building their magnetic observatory; Amundsen had had them built with copper nails, since iron ones would affect the magnetic needles. He had even brought with him slabs of marble on which the scientific instruments could be mounted precisely. These marble slabs were set with great care on a firm rock foundation. Captain Amundsen had provided himself with a complete set of the most accurate instruments.

The following days were spent laying in a supply of fresh meat. One day Amundsen and two of his men were out hunting when one of them exclaimed, "There is a caribou!"

They all looked. On a distant hill a black object had appeared.

"That caribou walks on two legs," remarked one of Amundsen's companions. Four more two-legged caribous joined the first, and in a body five Eskimos advanced. They were armed with bows and arrows, but Amundsen ordered his own men to throw down their rifles, as a token of friendliness. The Eskimos hesitated a moment. Then the leader uttered a gruff command and they all threw away their bows and arrows.

Amundsen welcomed them to the ship, showing them the marvels of its equipment. Thus began a friendship which was to last for the length of Amundsen's stay. The explorer always treated his Eskimo friends with the greatest consideration; and as for them, they worshipped him. The Eskimos asked if they might not bring their tribe and settle near the ship. Soon fifty Eskimo huts sprang up around the explorer's camp, housing a population of about two hundred men, women, and children.

This was the opportunity Amundsen had been seeking. For when he planned the expedition, he hoped that he would have the good fortune to study the customs of the natives. Perhaps he might succeed in acquiring a complete collection for a museum, illustrating every aspect of the Eskimo's life. Amundsen had therefore brought many things for the purpose of barter, and before he bade his Eskimo friends farewell, the set of exhibits he collected contained samples of suits of clothing worn by them, their cooking implements, their bows and arrows, spears, sleds, and canoes.

"What skill they have!" admired Amundsen. "Especially in working caribou skins into clothes. How cleverly their beadwork is fashioned, made from the teeth and bits of dried bone of the caribou!"

What fascinated him most was the way they stretched and twisted the bones of freshly killed game into spearheads, needles, and other very useful articles.

While Amundsen went about charting the coast of King William Land, his scientific needles kept recording day and night the behavior of the nearby Magnetic Pole. As every navigator knows, the compass does not point true north. Since the earth acts as a huge magnet, the place toward which the magnetic needle points is the Magnetic Pole. In days past, when he had sailed through Peel Sound around Prescott Island, Amundsen had been made aware of the near presence of the Magnetic Pole by the fantastic way his compass acted. Finally, the compass had become paralyzed. They might as well have tried to steer through the fog by a stick, and it was a miracle that the little party had found their way at last to King William Land. For nineteen months during the expedition of 1903–1905, Amundsen's instruments were active, and at length proved what scientists had long suspected, that the poles of that great magnet, the earth, are not fixed spots but are forever shifting their ground.

The rest of the Northwest Passage was still to be found. In August, 1905, the explorers again set sail, heading through Simpson Strait. Amundsen had calculated carefully how the mysterious passage must wind, but he would not be able to tell whether he had passed through it except by the sight of whaling vessels. That would tell him he was along the northern coast of Alaska at last.

Day after day for three weeks, the *Gjöa* crept along the dangerous shoals of the Straits. Amundsen was constantly sounding the depth with the lead, seeking a channel to carry him through into the known waters to the west. No one had charted this shallow passageway before. At one time the *Gjöa* traversed one portion of the channel with just one inch of water to spare beneath the keel.

Amundsen was torn with doubt. "It is true," he thought, "that I have laid my plans carefully. But so did the other explorers who perished here." He could neither eat nor sleep. Every nerve was strained as he strove to avoid the dangers that had swallowed up John Franklin and the rest.

"I *must* succeed," he told himself.

Then one day came the welcome sight. "A sail! A sail!"

He *had* succeeded. In the west, the glorious sight of a whaler enchanted his eyes. Alaska! Of the numberless possible channels winding between the maze of islands off the northern coast of North America, Amundsen had selected the right ones. The Northwest Passage from Europe to Asia was mapped.

III

A greater adventure was to come.

Amundsen began to lay plans for a heroic risk — the discovery of the North Pole! Hundreds of brave men had died in the attempt, and Amundsen realized that he might be added to the list of the dead. Truly Nature was guarding this secret with every weapon — with blizzards, fogs, terrible cold, scarcity of food, and the long polar night. Nevertheless, Amundsen, the scientific explorer, had weapons, too.

But just as he was ready to begin the struggle, news reached the world that the North Pole had been discovered. The American, Robert E. Peary, had won the prize, and the struggle of four hundred years to reach the North Pole was ended.

Amundsen was not disappointed. "There still is work for me," he said. "I shall be the first to reach the South Pole. I shall have an opportunity to study Antarctica, a continent probably larger than all of Europe. There is much work there for an explorer."

Antarctica, the seventh continent, was practically unknown before the beginning of the twentieth century. Captain Cook had crossed the Antarctic Circle in search of it, and was deterred from sailing onward only because his vessel was not equipped for the polar sea, with its cold and its icebergs. Cook had, however, predicted truly that such a continent existed.

Amundsen knew that a study of the climate of this ice-covered continent would be of the greatest help to the science of weather. His stay in Antarctica would hence be an extremely busy one. He would note the temperature, take magnetic observations, and map as much of the surface of the land as he could, while he was attempting to reach the South Pole.

In August, 1910, he was ready. During the Antarctic summer, he arrived in the Bay of Whales, in the South

Polar regions. There he faced the problem of choosing a place for his camp.

"The air currents in the Antarctic make the weather much more severe on the land than on ice. We shall, therefore, camp not on the land but on this glacier," Amundsen explained to his men. "And its high walls of ice will protect us from the terrific blizzards of the Antarctic with its world's worst climate."

But some scientists had said that camping on a glacier was certain death, because at any moment the ice might split and float away.

"Yet," thought Amundsen, "here is a part of the glacier which is caught fast. It has not moved, as I have read, for sixty-eight years. It seems safe enough."

He was right; the glacier made a cosy little home. The scene was beautiful in its vast whiteness. A clear sky and a glorious moon revealed the glistening landscape. Here and there a seal slouched about on the ice. The aurora shone brilliantly.

The time came for the great march to the South Pole. But Amundsen did not undertake to do it all at once. That would be too dangerous, for hundreds of miles separated him from the Pole, and, like other explorers, he might starve to death on the way. No, he had a cunning plan. All along the way he set up small camps stored with provisions and marked with flags and signposts so that they could be found later even in dense fog. Then he returned to the main camp, rested, harnessed up his dogs, and set out.

The plan worked perfectly. He reached the South Pole on December 14, 1911. There he camped for three days and explored the neighborhood for ten miles around. Then he returned with perfect ease and safety, his camps along the way supplying him constantly. In ninety-nine days he had made a journey of eighteen hundred and sixty miles through a maze of glaciers, over plateaus ten thousand feet high and across perilous crevasses. The expedition had been scientifically planned.

In everything he did, Amundsen was the scientist. For instance, much exploration was still needed in the North Pole regions. Thought Amundsen, "The day of the slow vessel and the slow dog sledge is over. I shall go to the North Pole in an airship. From the air I shall be able to survey the entire region of the Pole, and make my observations of the land and the winds more easily and truly."

So the world owes another debt to Amundsen. He and his crew were the first to fly over the North Pole in an airship, the *Norge,* and to bring back the information scientists wanted.

IV

In 1927, Amundsen wrote a book. In it he said, "My life as an explorer is closed. My honors are great. But there is nothing more that I am able to do."

He was wrong. His greatest deed of heroism was yet to come. And for it, the world will forever revere the man even more than it will the explorer.

In 1928, a member of the crew of the *Norge,* Nobile by name, went independently of Amundsen to the North Pole in the airship *Italia.* For a time all seemed to go well with him. Every day radio messages from the

Italia assured the world of its safety. One day the messages suddenly ceased.

"The *Italia* is down!" flashed across the newspapers.

Nobile and his men were perhaps dead somewhere in the Arctic regions. There was a bare chance that they were still alive in the ice fields. Who would risk his life to find them? Several searching parties went out immediately. Days passed, and the searching parties reported that they could not locate the unfortunate Nobile.

"If only Amundsen would go!" everybody prayed. "Only he can save the wrecked men."

Amundsen did not need to be asked. Although he was fifty-five years old and the doctors had forbidden him to face the rigors of exploration any more, he felt that he could not allow a human being to perish if he could help to save him.

The world watched Amundsen mount his airplane and soar northward into the sky. As he disappeared from view, everyone felt the greatness of the hero. For a while there was no news. Then suddenly one of the many searching parties sent the triumphant message, "Nobile saved."

The world rejoiced. The search was ended. But where was Amundsen? Why did he not come home too? Why did he not send a message? Every question was met with the frozen silence of the North. The world grew alarmed.

"Never fear," some said confidently, "there is no force that can down Amundsen. He who conquered the Northwest Passage and the South Pole does not die so easily."

Months passed without a trace of him. Governments

sent out expeditions in search of him. Every country wanted the honor of saving him. In vain. At length, when every region of the Arctic seemed to have been searched, the world gave up in despair and mourning.

His body has disappeared from the face of the earth. There, in the Arctic world, where his life work began, it ended.

BOOK II
Heroes
of Pure Science

Nicholas Copernicus

(1473–1543)

A NEW HEAVEN AND
A NEW EARTH

I

LET US imagine that we are taking the "grand tour" of Europe in the memorable year 1492.

As tourists, we visit the famed University of Paris. It seems a strange place indeed. Here in the heart of France, French is not spoken. The textbooks are in Latin. The students are expected to converse in Latin, and all the lectures are in Latin. Furthermore, through all Europe, every important university is an island of Latin.

We wonder: what sort of science does the University of Paris offer in the year 1492? We note that there are lectures in the sciences. But we find no laboratories, and we see no one attempting to perform experiments.

Let us join the students, for the physics lecture is about to start. The professor, wearing the scholar's cap and a magnificent gown and hood, is evidently discussing some difficult ideas that are in the textbook. The book is *Physics,* and its author is the Greek philosopher and scientist Aristotle, who wrote it about eighteen hundred years before this time.

You whisper to a student who is taking notes on the professor's lecture, "Aren't there any newer books on the sciences?"

"Yes," he replies, "but they only attempt to explain what Aristotle wrote."

"Haven't there been any new discoveries or new ideas since Aristotle?"

"Nothing that is really important. You'll find nearly everything you need in Aristotle."

What a strange science class!

Let us not be too discouraged. We'll try the lecture in astronomy. We see standing on a raised platform the lecturer, wearing his impressive regalia. "Remember," he tells his listeners, "that the sun, the moon, the five planets and the stars revolve around the earth. The earth is the center of the universe. Since a circle is the perfect geometric figure, therefore the paths of all the heavenly bodies must be circles."

You ask, "What textbook do you use in astronomy?"

The young man sitting beside you on the bench looks at you, amazed. "Ptolemy's book, the *Almagest*. Everyone knows the book, of course. For thirteen hundred years now, Ptolemy has been the trusted master in astronomy."

"Don't astronomers observe the stars and the planets?"

"There are some who do. There are a few minor corrections in Ptolemy's table of the positions of the planets at various times. We need that information to improve the calendar." Then, as an afterthought: "The ones who observe the planets more than any other group are the astrologers. Incidentally, the lectures of the professor of astrology are very interesting, and are certainly useful."

II

At the time of Ptolemy, there were records of the many observations made by the ancient astronomers. But the astronomers were puzzled by their own observations. The "wandering stars," the planets, appeared to move in complicated paths across the night sky throughout the course of a year. For instance, the planet Mars seems to move for some months at a steady pace. Then to slow down, stand still, and even move backward for a time.

"How can that be?" wondered the astronomers. The planets were not the only problem. Even the sun and the moon occasionally appeared to wander off from where they should have been.

In Alexandria, Ptolemy studied the perplexities of the astronomers. "All the heavenly bodies ought to move grandly at a steady pace," he said. "Undoubtedly, the sun, moon and the five planets do move in circular courses around the earth, which is the center of the universe. Perhaps the path of a planet is not an ordinary simple circle. Suppose, as the planet follows its circular path, the path digresses into a loop. Then after the planet has journeyed along the loop and has come back to the main circle, there will be other loops that it must follow. How well does this theory account for the observations of the astronomers?"

To answer this question Ptolemy had to do a tremendous amount of calculation. With his theory, however, he could state the positions of the sun, the moon, and the planets in the heavens for different times of the year. His reward was that his calculated positions agreed substantially with the records of the observations of astronomers. Ptolemy now organized the data that had been gathered through the centuries. He brought the records up to date, and he set down the positions of the stars and other heavenly bodies according to the time of year in his great book, the *Almagest*.

The wonderful thing about Ptolemy's tables was that they were approximately correct. The planets always were somewhere near the place that Ptolemy's tables foretold they would be — somewhere near, though not quite on the spot. But the difference bothered nobody. For once, the mystery of the heavens was clearing up. And Ptolemy was the man who had shown that the universe was not a mystery. No wonder everybody had faith in Ptolemy, and refused to believe anybody else.

So thirteen centuries went by, and in the schools, Ptolemy's word was unquestioned.

III

In 1492, at the time Columbus was discovering the New World, Nicholas Copernicus, son of a successful Polish merchant, was studying at the University of Krakow. He was preparing himself to give the world "a new heaven." He then went to Italy, the center of learning, where he stayed ten years, first as a student, then as a teacher.

His zeal for learning, it seems, knew no bounds. He mastered all studies: law, medicine, natural science, mathematics. He was a skillful painter. He was expert in political science, and was appointed a member of the Council of German States. He was also translator of books from the Greek.

His greatest interest lay in astronomy. In this study, however, he was extremely handicapped. For there were no telescopes, nor any of the instruments we have today for observing the heavens. The few instruments he used he had to make himself.

"Why do you have to worry about astronomy?" everybody said. "Ptolemy has said the last word on that subject."

Nobody gave Copernicus any encouragement.

He looked long at Ptolemy's picture of the heavens. "Is it not queer," he thought, "that although all the planets move differently and are in different positions and of different sizes, yet they all seem to go round the earth once a day. It is incredible!"

The more he pondered, the more incredible it seemed. One day a strange idea came to him. "If the earth spun around like a top once every day, then the planets would all seem to be turning around the earth once every day. That I can understand."

People laughed at the idea. "The earth moves! You must be joking, for that is contrary to common sense. If the earth moved, you could feel the motion." But Copernicus knew that if you were sailing on a smooth sea and you looked at the floor of your cabin, you could not detect any motion. Gaze out from the deck at the scenery, and you do see movement. But which is moving: you, or the scenery? Just so, if the earth were moving, the only way Ptolemy could observe it was by looking at the heavens, and then he thought it was the heavens that moved.

"Perhaps the earth does move!"

But the people of "common sense" had another objection.

"If a large body like the earth moved," they said, "it would travel with such speed that if you shot an arrow into the air, the earth would rush past under it before the arrow came down. Or if you jumped very high, the earth would whiz by, leaving you in the air. Since this does not happen, the earth does not move."

But if you are sitting in your cabin, and you drop a penny, will it not fall at your feet? The penny will not be left in the air. It has the same motion as the cabin.

"Surely the earth moves," said Copernicus confidently. "It must, because it solves the problem of motion in the universe so simply."

But the followers of Ptolemy were not so easily convinced. "Absurd!" they insisted. "A moving earth would fly to pieces."

"Why should it?" retorted Copernicus. "The stars in your moving heavens — do they fly to pieces?"

Copernicus now used his mathematics. From youth to middle age he worked constantly to prove his theory. Then he wrote his conclusions in a book, which he did not publish until the very end of his life. He might not even then have done so, for he was modest and very shy. His time was spent in ministering to the sick and poor, and he would have been content to end his days so, but for some friends who were ambitious for him and urged him to publish his thoughts on the universe. And fortunate it is for us that they did. Copernicus always thought, "I am not ready yet. I can better my book. I shall wait . . ." And he might have kept on waiting to the end and never given us the book which proved one of the greatest events in the history of the world. It revolutionized our whole thinking.

To begin with, Copernicus proved Ptolemy wrong. The earth must move, because only then could the changing positions of all the stars, the seasons of the year, and the changes of night and day all occur simultaneously. The earth, Copernicus showed, is one of the planets. All the planets move around the sun, which is the center. "Imagine a series of circles," said Copernicus, "one inside the other. The circles are the paths that the planets follow around the center point — the sun. As for our earth, it spins around like a top once a day, while at the same time, it makes a journey around the sun that lasts a year. The spin gives us day and night. The motion around the sun gives us our seasons."

Thoughtful men saw how accurate, simple, and beautiful Copernicus had made everything, while Ptolemy had complicated the motions of the planets and had been inaccurate in the bargain.

The wonder of this solar system, as we now call it, was grasped slowly. What staggered everybody was the immensity of the universe as Copernicus pictured it. Before his time the earth was regarded as the largest body in the heavens. We now know that the extent of our universe is terrifying to imagine. We have counted thousands of millions of stars, the light from which takes thousands of years to reach our eyes. Copernicus himself did not realize how vast was the space he had

opened up. Beyond the stars we can see with our naked
eye are vast star clusters and nebulae that give forth
light which, traveling at 186,000 miles a second, takes
millions and millions of years to strike the earth. And
we know that our sun, which is more than a million
times as large as the earth, is only an average-size star.

Suddenly a scandal arose. "What!" everybody cried.
"The earth not the center of the universe! We great
men not the center of attraction! We won't believe it.
You say we are of insignificant size, you ask us away
from our shining center, you make us wobble around
the sun, like a moth around a lamp. Outrageous!"

Alas, what could Copernicus do? Truth is truth. He
had drawn a new world for an old, a beautiful and precise one for a cumbrous and inexact one. And still people refused to accept it because it hurt their pride.

They were helpless, however, before the mathematics of Copernicus. He could prove his theory, but one
had to know a great deal about mathematics to understand the proof. So the world still doubted, and it was
left for another hero to convince us that Copernicus
was right.

Scarcely had he given his consent to the publication
of his book when he was stricken with paralysis. On
May 24, 1543, just a few hours before he died, the
printer placed the book in his hands. His life's end was
the beginning of his immortality.

Years after, when Tycho Brahe, a great astronomer
and follower of Copernicus, was given the wooden instruments with which Copernicus had discovered a
new heaven, he said: "Copernicus has been able to stop
the sun in its path across the sky, and has made the im-

movable earth move about the sun in a circle. About the earth he caused the moon to turn; he has changed for us the very face of the universe. He has done what was not permitted any other mortal to do since the beginning of the world. . . ."

Galileo Galilei

(1564–1642)

THE FATHER OF
TELESCOPIC ASTRONOMY

I

In the late dusk of an afternoon about 1582, a young student of medicine at the University of Pisa in Italy was kneeling at prayer in the cathedral there. Galileo Galilei, as the Italian youth was named, or simply Galileo, as he is called today, rose at last to go when his glance fell upon the bronze lamp which hung over him in the center of the dim sanctuary.

The attendant had come to light the lamp, and in order to do so more easily had drawn it towards himself. As he released it finally, it began swinging to and fro. Galileo watched keenly.

And so watching, it struck him that while the swinging grew less and less as it died down, the time of each swing neither diminished nor increased. At least so it seemed. But how could he be sure? There were no watches in those days. How could he measure accurately the length of the time it took the swinging object to make each swing? His heart beat excitedly. . . . Ah! The beat in his body! It ticked regularly. For a timepiece he could use his pulse.

So he did. And he found he was right: it took the *same time* for the lamp to make its first largest movement as the last faint tremor. The swing was as regular as the beat of his pulse.

He looked up. . . . Something stirred in his mind. He hurried home at once, and then and there began his famous career of invention which the world forever will celebrate. It also occurred to Galileo that if a pulse beat could time a swinging object, a swinging object could also time a pulse!

The result of this reflection was the first instrument for the use of doctors for taking the pulse of a patient, and the first mechanical device ever made to help a doctor treat the human body. In so many swings of the pulsilogia, for so he called his instrument, a healthy pulse beats a definite number of times, just as nowadays we know that in sixty seconds a healthy pulse beats about seventy-two times.

Galileo himself was destined never to use his pulsilogia as a doctor. In his third year at the university, he happened to attend some lectures on geometry by a visiting mathematician. Galileo had never studied mathematics in school. He was so fascinated with geometry that he abandoned medicine, and from then on, heart and soul, he devoted himself to mathematics.

II

When he invented the pulsilogia, Galileo was eighteen, having been born in Pisa in 1564, the same year as Shakespeare, and three days before the death of Michelangelo. As a child he distinguished himself by his cleverness in building all kinds of toys.

"He is a born engineer," thought his father.

But no! For when it came to music, which his father, a noted musician, taught him, the young Galileo displayed a finer touch than his teacher on the lute and the organ.

"Ah," thought his delighted father, "he will some day play before princes."

But there again, just when he thought his son's career settled, a new talent began to flower in the youth — painting.

"Well, then — painting let it be," said the perplexed father.

Yes, but what about the youth's poetry?

"Settle it once for all," cried the bewildered father. "Become a businessman, a doctor — anything!"

Galileo decided for himself in this as he did in all things. He had been captivated by the art of mathematics, and he determined to follow science, the language of which is mathematics.

At college, he was dubbed the "Wrangler," because he asked and argued questions which embarrassed his professors. But instead of being encouraged for his cleverness and originality, he was frequently made to suffer for these traits, for learning then, especially in science, was a strange affair. The greatest scientist known up to that time had been the ancient Greek philosopher Aristotle. If Aristotle said a thing, that thing was settled. Aristotle was never doubted. Nobody thought of putting *his* word to any test. In fact, if you questioned the word of Aristotle, people became suspicious of you at once. What did you mean, they asked. Were you trying to be different from everybody else?

Aristotle had said, for instance, that if you dropped a ten-pound weight and a one-pound weight at the same time, the ten-pounder would fall ten times as fast as the one-pounder. For eighteen hundred years everybody believed this, but no one thought of testing it.

No one but Galileo, that is. He had devised some ingenious experiments that showed conclusively that Aristotle was mistaken. Galileo was now a professor of mathematics, and he announced one day to his students that two bodies, falling through space at the same time, reached ground at the same time, regardless of their weight. Furthermore, he invited everybody to witness the trial of Aristotle's saying about falling bodies.

So one morning, around the famous Leaning Tower of Pisa, there was a great stir of people. Professor mingled with student, cleric with layman, on that day. All had gathered to witness the contest which would decide the downfall of either Aristotle's principle or Galileo's teaching. Which was it to be? Aristotle, the renowned sage, or Galileo Galilei, a mere youth of twenty-five? It seemed an unequal match.

"The youth is headstrong as well as deluded," sneered one townsman politely.

"He won't go far with such crazy notions," rejoined another, shrugging his shoulders. "As you will soon see," he added, pointing to the tower.

The students, however, who liked Galileo, were anxious.

"Would to Heaven," you could hear them say, "that Maestro Galileo might succeed."

Meanwhile the figure of Galileo, with stocky frame and reddish head, was showing itself on the top of the tower. In his left hand he balanced a ten-pound shot; in his right, a one-pound shot. The crowd below became tense. A shout went up as he suddenly let go of the shots. The two weights cut the air, and — to the greater glory of Galileo — both struck the earth at the same time, just as he had said they would.

A few diehard Aristotelians refused to believe their own eyes. They even accused Galileo of using magic. Nevertheless, from this time on, though he continued to be opposed more bitterly than ever, partly from ignorance, partly from envy, he leaped into fame at home and abroad. In fact, his popularity all over Europe was such that often his lectures could not be given indoors, so large were the crowds that wanted to hear him.

But what a disturbing fellow he was! Just when you thought you had learned something from the books of some ancient philosopher, along came Galileo, not at all abashed by the reputation of your philosopher, and tried out the idea with his hands and eyes. Likely as not, he proved that what you had learned was worthless.

One evening, for instance, Galileo was at the palace of the Grand Duke of Tuscany. Among the guests were a few scientists. ". . . Ice, now," someone happened to remark, "is condensed water and —"

"No, it isn't," said Galileo abruptly. "It's rarefied water. That's the reason ice is lighter than water."

"Ice lighter than water! What an idea! Read your Aristotle, my friend."

"Aristotle," replied Galileo calmly, "was a very great

man, but he made many mistakes. If ice is heavier than water, why does it float?"

"That depends," retorted his opponent, "on the shape of the ice — as Aristotle says."

Galileo did not argue. There was a way to decide any question — experiment. In a basin of water he put some ice. "Choose your shape," he invited. The result was undeniable. No matter what the shape, the piece of ice floated. It was lighter than water. That was Galileo's way. In scientific matters he cared not a rap for authority.

A powerful lord of Italy, one of the Medici family, invented a dredging machine. He sent a model of it to Galileo for his opinion. Now Galileo was living in poverty, and here was his chance to win favor. Here it was indeed, but the young scientist rejected it because it meant that he would have to stoop to flattery and lies.

"Your machine is worthless," he said bluntly.

The nobleman was furious, and built his machine defiantly. That did him no good, however. The machine would not work.

In the meantime, Galileo continued work on his own mechanical inventions. At this time the most noted among these was the sector, which is used even yet by draughtsmen. In all Europe demand for his instruments sprang up, and to such an extent that Galileo opened a workshop for their manufacture.

III

One summer day, the news reached him that an optician in Holland, Hans Lippersheim, had made a startling discovery. He had been looking through two lenses, holding one close to his eye and the other at arm's length. Peering through both at once, he was amazed to find that objects appeared upside down and larger than usual. The reason for this peculiar fact he did not know, nor could anybody tell him.

So much Galileo heard. The wonder of it! Under your very eyes an object grew larger! Distant things came nearer! What secret of Nature was hidden there?

Galileo spent the night thinking. "Two pieces of glass," he reasoned. "Should they be flat, convex, or concave? Not flat, because flat glass does not bend the rays of light that pass through it. Well, then: two concave lenses, two convex, or one of each — which should it be? Let's see . . ."

On the following day, he had not only discovered the reason why a spyglass brings an object nearer, but also had made one which far surpassed in power the original glass of the Dutchman. Galileo's glass, moreover, showed the object upright.

But he was not satisfied. He worked for perfection. Within six months he had created a telescope which magnified an object a thousand times, making it appear more than thirty times nearer. With this powerful instrument, he gazed overhead into the skies, and things undreamed of began to glimmer and whirl and wink down on him.

He turned his glass on the moon. The ancients had stated that the moon was polished and smooth. Yet there, before Galileo's eyes, was the surface of the moon, rough with deep shadows and highlights. What did these shadows mean? "Mountains on the moon," concluded Galileo. "The moon is a body similar to the earth; only, as Copernicus says, it turns around the earth."

The world began to take an interest. The stargazer turned to the sun. He looked and was puzzled. The glorious lamp of heaven was spotted and blotched. And day after day, as he stared at them, the spots seemed to move and disappear around the rim of the sun. Then some of them reappeared on the opposite side. What did *that* mean?

"The sun is a sphere. It rotates on its axis as does the earth, but much more slowly," announced Galileo. "The sun completes an entire revolution in about a month."

But the glory of the heavens first burst forth when Galileo trained his spyglass on that cloudy expanse known as the Milky Way. Everybody who looked up at the heavens at night had marveled at the bluish-white stretch, like a ribbon across the sky.

"What is it?" they asked.

"Thousands of stars, too far away to be seen by the eye alone," was Galileo's answer.

The world was breathless with excitement. Galileo was discovering the hidden universe! But the most amazing spectacle came on the night of January 7, 1610. The discoverer that night turned his attention to the planet Jupiter. He was a little surprised to see three bright stars near the planet, two stars on one side, and one on the other side. It was nothing unusual that he should discover a few more stars. But the next night he found that these three stars were in different positions. All were on the same side of Jupiter! Galileo was astounded. And what was his excitement when one of the stars disappeared around the edge of Jupiter! A few nights later he saw four stars where before there had been three.

Galileo was no longer in any doubt and made the announcement: "There are four moons wheeling around Jupiter. Jupiter has four satellites." His glass was not strong enough to see the other eight moons which have since been discovered.

Intelligent people were now awakened to the beauty and mystery of the heavenly bodies. Everyone wanted a telescope. The Queen of France, when hers came, shocked the court by falling on her knees with excitement, so great was her impatience to see Jupiter's moons, and the mountains on our earthly moon, and all the new worlds of Galileo. King Henry of France sent an order to Galileo for a star to be named after him. It was a matter of business with the king. He would pay for a star, as one pays for a rose. Let the star, preferably a nice big one, be named "Henry." Alas, the king had to do without his star.

To the mass of people, Galileo had simply opened the heavens and shown new stars, spots on the sun, and other such wonders. But for scientists he had done a far more significant thing — he had proved beyond any doubt that Copernicus was right. He had answered the sneer of the enemies of Copernicus, "Show us!"

"Those planets whirling around Jupiter furnish a model of our solar system," said Galileo, and it could not be denied.

But despite the worldwide chant in praise of Galileo, the hero's way was by no means rosy. His old antagonists, the Aristotelians, had the usual weapon of refusing to admit what they saw with their eyes. "The lenses in Galileo's telescope cause many illusions," they said. "These new planets cannot exist. Why, Aristotle does not mention them." Many refused even to put their eye to the telescope. "I will never admit the existence of those moons of Jupiter," each said.

"Don't look with Aristotle's eyes. Use your own eyes," Galileo pleaded in vain.

In addition to such prejudice and envy, Galileo began to suffer from an illness which affected his eyes. Nevertheless, Galileo was steadily working on the book that he had been dreaming about since he was a young man. *Dialogues of the Two Greatest Systems of the World,* he named it. He wrote his book in Italian instead of Latin so that everyone could read it.

In it, he imagines a series of conversations between three gentlemen, two of them arguing for the ideas of Copernicus and Galileo, and the third, who is a follower of Aristotle, only agreeing to what the other two say if he can find it in Aristotle or in some other ancient book. In the *Dialogues,* Galileo describes his discoveries in astronomy and the results of his lifelong experiments on motion and rest. When this book was published in 1632, it created a sensation.

Galileo's health had been declining. His eldest daughter, whom he loved dearly, died. In his extreme affliction he sought comfort in more work. "Work, and you forget your troubles," he was fond of saying over and over again.

IV

While king and peasant alike were watching the dazzling new stars which Galileo had shown them, the great master himself was engaged in a strange experiment. Galileo would roll a carefully made round bronze ball along a smooth polished board. He would tip the board a little, then roll the ball down. This he repeated over and over, each time inclining the board a bit more, until it was vertical. And each time he estimated how long it took for the ball to reach ground. It went faster and faster, he noticed, the more the board was inclined toward the vertical.

Repeatedly, Galileo would put two boards together in the shape of a V, start the ball down one side, and note the time required to make the descent. He repeated the experiment to the precision of one-tenth of a pulsebeat.

Queer doings these, but Galileo had an uncanny feeling that the mystery of the heavens could be solved by such humble experiments.

"A ball rolls along a path; a planet goes around the sun," thought Galileo. "Why? How? That question we must settle: *how* things move." That was Galileo's greatest moment of genius. No one before had ever dreamed that there was a science of motion — dynamics, as it is called.

"Motion!" people exclaimed. "What is difficult about that? A thing moves because — well, because something else pushes it. Some force, you see, makes it move. It is so with the planets. Some force is continually shoving them around and around."

When Galileo finished his ball playing, he retorted, "Once a thing is moving, you don't need a force to keep it in motion. It will go on by itself forever. On the contrary, you need a force to stop it."

"How can that be?" objected his bewildered students. "When the board was held in a horizontal position, the ball gradually came to a stop."

"That," replied Galileo, "was because there was a force stopping the ball — the friction of the board against it. But when there is no friction, as in the sky, the moving body moves on forever."

Galileo wrote up his experiments in another book, *"The Two New Sciences,"* his last and greatest. This book has since become the scientist's guide to the "experimental method."

In a letter of July 4, 1637, to a friend, Galileo wrote, "The sight of my right eye, that eye whose labors have had such glorious results, is lost forever. . . ."

Six months passed and he was totally blind. Then it was that the great English poet John Milton visited him, not realizing that he, too, was destined to become blind.

The last glimpse we get of Galileo is impressive. He is trying to complete an invention before death overtakes him. On the day of his death, January 8, 1642, he is explaining to his son plans for a pendulum clock based on his youthful observation of the lamp in the cathedral of Pisa.

Christian Huygens

(1629–1695)

INVENTOR, DREAMER,
MATHEMATICIAN

I

IN THE COUNTRY of Judea, one day about two thousand years ago, two servants met and spoke together thus:

First Servant: Is it really true what they say about you?

Second Servant: Certainly. At the king's court, I was a timepiece, and was treated pretty well. At night and mealtimes, I was relieved by my brother, who was also a timepiece, just as my father was in his day. Indeed, I come of a family of timepieces.

First Servant: How's that? Have you no sand for hourglasses in your country, that you must tell time by men?

Second Servant: What! We, no sand! Enough . . . But the king is more precise about the time of day than other people. No hourglass for him! The human pulse, when it is healthy, is much more accurate than your trickling sand. As for sundials — what good are they when the sun doesn't choose to shine?

In this way does a German author describe the ancient attempts to measure time.

There was one other and more successful way than any of these, however: the water timer. That the regular trickle and flow of water marks the passing hours is an old human experience. Time flows as well as flies.

> Men may come and men may go
> But I go on forever —

is the song of the brook.

"You lose water," is a Roman rebuke to an idler. Even today we sometimes hear it said, "Much water has flowed under the bridge since I last saw you."

It was quite natural, therefore, to place a basin filled with water in such a way that it would empty itself from sunrise to sunrise. It would have been awkward to try to carry a basin of water for a timepiece in your vest pocket, of course, and you could not have been sure of keeping a precise engagement for lunch by it. But then, no one expected you to do that. It was enough that you could vaguely know the passing of your day. When the basin was half empty, you supposed that the day was half gone.

Later, it occurred to someone to put an iron float in the water, and on the basin a face with twenty-four circles, one for each hour. A dial on the face was connected with the float, which, as it sank with the falling water, moved the dial across the circles. And as it came to each circle or hour, the dial released a metal ball which dropped on a pan, sounding a note like a bell.

"A clock!" people called this time machine, for the word *clock* comes from a word meaning *bell*.

The water clock was a great advance over the sand-glass. It counted each hour of the day. But still you could not have depended much on it if you had had to make the twelve-fifty-four train. Fortunately, in those days there were no trains. So, to the workman, in a world which moved slowly, without railroads and modern industry, the exact time of the day was of little importance. To the king, it was of some importance. But if you happened to be an astronomer in the days following Copernicus, this lack of an accurate measure of minutes and seconds crippled your work, for in observing the stars even a few seconds are of tremendous importance.

Galileo felt the handicap and in the last years of his life began work on a new kind of clock that would tell not only the hours but the minutes and the seconds. It would run not by water or sand but by the swing of a pendulum.

The prospect of a clock so exact filled scientists with delight. What a boon it would be! They were sure to have it, too, for what the great Galileo undertook, he did not fail to accomplish. Suddenly, with the death of Galileo, the prize seemed to be snatched right away from the outstretched hands of the world.

Who could finish what Galileo had begun? Where was the genius to fill the great gap, from what country would he come, from what family? The stage was empty and all eyes fixed upon it when out stepped the Dutchman, Christian Huygens.

Christian's father, Constantine, was one of Holland's most illustrious noblemen and brilliant poets. At his wish, his son took up the study of law. But the young man was too keenly interested in every other branch of study not to stray from his law books. He strayed so often, in fact, that father Huygens ruefully decided it would be best if his eager and pleasant son abandoned law for something more to his liking.

But what? Like Galileo, Christian was an accomplished musician; he was an able biologist — the study of living things fascinated him. But — there again, like Galileo — the subject to which he turned most gladly was mathematics, the language of science, and heart and soul he gave himself up to it.

In a short while, the youth's discoveries attracted the attention of the philosophers. To be sure, the world of people on the street did not yet hear of him. His thoughts were not yet their thoughts.

"The larger the diameter of a circle, the larger the circumference; what is the relation between these two? . . . Look at the end of that spoke in the wagon wheel turning down the road! What kind of curve is it writing in the air? . . . How did the whirling earth come to have flat poles? . . ."

In the footsteps of Galileo, Huygens' path led him to a study of the heavens. Here the old bother of having no exact clock plagued him. He was stuck just where Galileo had been.

"There is no use going on," he thought, "until I settle the problem of the clock."

He adopted his master's idea of the pendulum. "The

shorter the pendulum," he knew, "the faster it will swing back and forth. Also, the whole business depends on what sort of curve the pendulum swings in."

With these two beliefs he went to work. Years passed. The world had almost forgotten its dream of having an accurate clock when in June, 1657, Christian Huygens came forward with the first pendulum clock. No more hopeless guesses about seconds of time! Let the world move as fast as it would, it had the sanction of Christian Huygens' pendulum clock.

His discoveries in mathematics and physics were published in his book called *The Treatise on the Pendulum Clock.*

There was one trouble: the pendulum was not a good sailor. On the lurching deck of a ship, it was of no more use than a water clock. To invent a seafaring clock meant more hard work for the young scientist, but in the end, he devised the great scheme of replacing the pendulum with a coiled spring. His design of a spiral spring combined with a balance wheel is the main idea of our modern watch.

II

Now that he had a good clock, Huygens was ready to time the stars in their movement across the heavens. But here the way was barred: Galileo's telescope was too weak to show any new sights. And there was no use trying to make the telescope larger, for beyond a certain size, the lenses blurred the image as opera glasses do when they are not well focused. It was a serious matter. It meant that never, perhaps, would the far-lying stars be seen.

The genius of Galileo lived ardently in the mind of Huygens. He who made Galileo's dream of a pendulum clock a reality carried on the work to the telescope.

"Something is wrong with our way of grinding and polishing lenses," he decided.

In quick time he devised a new way. So amazing was its success that from a spyglass a few feet long, the new instrument became a telescope two hundred and ten feet long! Today, of course, the telescope has grown from a magnifier which an individual can manipulate and put to his eye, to a stupendous machine housed in a vaulted tower and moved by electric power; a man clambering on the largest one is as an insect on the leg of a table. But in Huygens' day, his telescope was nothing short of a miracle.

Scientific men, moreover, will always be grateful to Huygens for a very clever device. He marked off his telescope lens like a ruler. The result is that when you look through a telescope, the rulings appear to be on the surface of the body seen. By this means, you can judge the distances on the planets as though you were actually measuring them by a ruler.

The cloak of Galileo upon him, Huygens turned the clear eye of his telescope on the sky. He searched out the planet Saturn and there fixed his gaze. He remembered what a mystery Saturn had been to Galileo; how, one night, Galileo fancied he saw a moon on either side of Saturn. The Italian seer had been about to announce this confidently when to his astonishment the

moons changed into long arms that stretched straight
out from the edge of the planet. The mystery deepened
when he found the arms curved like handles. His bewilderment could have been no dizzier had he seen two
stars collide.

"The weakness of my intellect," Galileo wrote in
chagrin, "the terror of being mistaken, have greatly
confounded me."

Galileo had died and a generation of men had gone
by, but the mystery of Saturn remained unsolved until
Christian Huygens, armed with his new telescope, attacked it. His faith in his new glass was at stake; his
power as a scientist was at stake. Huygens peered
through the glass; he made out the splendid giant Saturn . . . An awesome, terrifying spectacle, for Saturn
is not a simple planet at all. It is a brilliant ball, girdled
with a huge ring and moons riding around it! A vision
to make Christian Huygens rub his eyes. There is nothing else like it in the sky. It looks like a heavenly
machine, or a magnificent toy of the gods.

"Saturn is girt with a ring," announced the discoverer simply, "and I have seen what was never before
seen, its brightest moon." We call that moon Titan.

The mystery of Saturn at last solved, the glass of
Huygens swept again over the face of the heavens. Now
there are in the sky strange forms, most of them invisible to the naked eye. They look like patches of cloud,
like mists in the sky. Some of them are thought to be
island universes similar to our galaxy. Nebulae, scientists call these distant worlds.

Some are round like spirals, others long and narrow.
Some have the shape of dumbbells, others of rings. So

far away are most of them that the light they shed has traveled a million years to reach us. The sky is strewn with these worlds; in fact, there exist hundreds of thousands of them, and the astronomer's task is to find and study them.

One winter's night, Huygens pointed his telescope into the southern skies, to a very bright group of stars known as the constellation Orion. The brightness of Orion was always a cause of marvel. Homer, for instance, speaking of the splendor of his hero Achilles, says that he shone "like the star which rises in autumn and sends its rays among many stars in the depth of the night, and is called the dog of Orion."

Huygens knew the stars of Orion well enough. So did everybody. But what no one had ever before noticed, and what Huygens now discovered in the constellation, was a wreath as of smoke.

"A nebula in Orion!"

III

Christian Huygens had at last become a great world figure. The Royal Society of England invited him to lecture to its members. Princes began to extend their favors to him. The King of France, in fact, lavished so much attention on him that the great scientist was induced for a while to settle in France.

For hard work as well as genius, his name was a byword. He excelled in everything, it seemed. Somehow he found time to become even a remarkable musician. There was also in his amiable, kind disposition a touch of the dreamer.

"To live on another planet," he often imagined, "would be a strange experience. Perhaps there *are* living beings on the other planets, millions of miles away from us. Why not? On Mars and Jupiter I can see shadows which must be water or clouds. And if there is water, why not plants and animals, and perhaps even man?" He did not know. He was just spinning out a reasonable thread of fancy. "What moonlight nights on Saturn, with its moons playing down their beams! Yet if you lived somewhere on the equator of Saturn just now, you would be in total darkness, for there I see the gigantic shadow of the ring."

His musings then turned to another planet: "How hot it is on Mercury! Three times nearer the sun than we are, Mercury is nine times hotter. But then, an inhabitant of Mercury, looking at the little dot in the sky known as Earth, must pity us for our cold and dreary light. So our light is in comparison to theirs! If we could pay Mercury a visit, our return to Earth would be like coming into a dim room from the bright sunshine."

On he dreamed for the space of a book, *The Celestial Worlds Discovered* — but not for longer. Soon he was grappling with one of the hardest questions of all time — what is light? Everyone has been out on a bright day and felt the pleasant heat of the sun. He has perhaps watched the world light up at dawn.

"But what causes the pleasant heat and the dawn?" scientists were asking. "What are sunbeams?"

Now Christian Huygens had often thrown stones into a lake and watched the ripples of water. He had seen the gentle waves form and travel until they reached shore. This, he believed, is the way light acts. Only at what a speed! Light waves travel as much as 186,000 miles every second.

By means of his famous "wave theory of light," Huygens worked out an entirely new branch of learning: the science of optics; and it is for this great work that modern scholars still study him.

Christian Huygens died on the eighth of June, 1695, at the Hague, bequeathing his inventions and discoveries which later heroes were to use in carrying forward the work of civilization.

Isaac Newton

(1642–1727)

THE PATHS OF THE PLANETS

I

WHEN Galileo died, he left a puzzle for the next generation. A body in motion, he taught, must continue to
move straight ahead forever. That is, provided there is
no friction to slow it down. And in the sky there is no
friction.

Following Galileo, scientists tried to make his laws of
motion explain the movements of the planets. "We can
now understand," they agreed, "why a moving planet
keeps moving. But why does it go in a circle around the
sun, and not in a straight line?"

A young scholar at Cambridge University, Isaac
Newton, thought about this — and then solved the
puzzle.

Isaac Newton was born in Woolsthorpe, England, in
1642, the year in which Galileo died. As a boy, young
Isaac was remembered chiefly for his ingenuity in constructing a variety of toys. For instance, at Woolsthorpe
the simple villagers still talked of that fearful sight in
the sky one night — a comet with a glowing tail, riding
in the sky over their heads. When the comet caught fire

it revealed itself as one of Isaac's kites with a paper lantern tied to its tail. Another time he made a windless windmill. He despised mills which depended on a fickle wind. So he built a toy mill of another kind. Inside his mill he put a mouse on a treadwheel. He called this mouse the miller, since it moved the mill and ate up the flour.

When he was doing his spelling lesson, questions not in the book would pop into his mind and interfere with his learning. "How fast is the wind blowing?" he wondered. "How can I measure the speed of the wind?"

At the cost of his spelling lesson, he found a way at last to test the wind. With his back to the breeze, he jumped as far forward as he could. He marked the spot "with the wind." Then he faced the breeze, and again jumped, this time "against the wind." After subtracting, the young scientist could speak gravely of a "stiff five-footer" or a "roaring eight-foot gale."

His lessons, of course, suffered from such preoccupation and he hovered somewhat nearer the tail than the head of his class. One day, the stimulus to become a good scholar came to him in the shape of a kick in the stomach. The foot that kicked him belonged to a bright bully who was ahead of Isaac in the class. In retaliation, Isaac first beat his antagonist with his fists. Then he began to beat him with his brain, and the speed that Isaac gathered in his studies, the acceleration as Galileo might have called it, carried him to the very head of his class and perhaps beyond his teacher.

Mrs. Newton, who owned a farm, hoped that her son would become a farmer. Isaac was therefore taken out of the grammar school and started on his career of tend-ing the cattle, weeding the vegetable patch, and taking his produce to sell at market. But the meadow was a pleasant place in which to model in wood with his knife, the vegetable patch was near a hedge where one could sit in the shade and solve problems in mathematics, and the marketplace was near his friend the apothecary who had interesting books. The result was that the weeds grew rank in the patch, the cattle ate the corn, and the customers bought elsewere. In despair, Mrs. Newton sent the bad farmer back to school where he could be more successful. He was successful, and in time went to Cambridge University where he found the works of Galileo.

II

"Why do planets move in a circle around the sun?" That question made Newton forget that he had not eaten dinner, or that he was going forth without a shirt. And the objection offered to Copernicus that a whirling earth would fly to pieces, Newton feared had not been answered any more than the question "Why does an apple fall down and not up?"

"Gravitation!" some called the force.

This was a vague answer, thought Newton. One might just as well say, "Abracadabra," if all he could answer was "Gravity." He must show exactly — with figures — how gravity works.

"Well, how does it work?" he questioned. "The moon goes round the earth, the apple falls to the earth . . . The earth must be forcing both the apple and the moon. But the moon does not fall down. Maybe that is because the moon is so much farther away than the apple . . . Ah, here's the story! The moon is trying to get past the earth, but the earth pulls upon it and, as it turns, pulls the moon round and round with it. In fact, the earth would pull the moon right down to it with a crash, as it does the apple, were not the moon, fortunately for us, too far away and traveling with a terrific speed past the earth. The pulling force of the earth becomes weaker and weaker as the body it pulls is farther and farther away. Now, how much weaker?"

The young scientist drew a few circles and made a few calculations. "I see it! If the moon is four times as far away as the apple, then four times four — you square the distance, which is sixteen, and use the inverse of it, one sixteenth — the earth exerts only one sixteenth of the force. The inverse square! That sounds plausible. But wait! Does not the moon or the apple have any say in the matter? Does not each return the pull? It must! Every body, even if it is a speck, draws every other body. The apple and the earth pull each other, but of course the apple is so small, it has little force. The moon and earth pull each other together. If they did not, the moon would fly away out into space. But no! The earth pulls it. That is why the moon must keep whirling around it."

The mathematics of his day was of little help to Newton. For instance, an astronomer records the time and the precise position of the moon every time that he makes an observation of it. There were countless such observations for the moon and the five planets then known. These eventually found their places in astronomical tables.

Newton was perplexed. He wanted to calculate how fast the moon must travel so that it should be in the precise location according to the astronomical tables. At the same time, he assumed that there is an inverse square pull of gravity. What kind of equations could he write that would state all these facts, and would allow for the moon's swing around the earth?

The mathematics that he needed, Newton reasoned, must be able to cope with the idea of a "rate of change." And a "rate of change" mathematics was exactly what he required in order to calculate the paths of the planets which speed around the sun at different rates.

Isaac Newton developed such a mathematics — the calculus.

III

"Now for the test," thought Newton. "The earth, the books say, is about twenty-one thousand miles in circumference. Then the distance of the moon from the earth is . . . At that rate, according to my reckoning, it should take the moon about thirty-two days to go once around the earth." Alas for Isaac Newton. It takes the moon only about twenty-seven days.

Newton felt defeated. All his eagerness to discover how gravitation works seemed like an empty dream, and he put away his papers. The sense of his failure lay upon him for sixteen years, until one day someone mentioned to him that a French scientist had discovered a mistake in the measurement of the earth.

"It is really twenty-five thousand miles around," Newton was told.

Home he rushed. Maybe he had been right after all. He must go over the figures again. The revised figures proved that he had been right after all, that he had discovered the law of gravitation sixteen years before. He could have shouted from the housetops: "I have discovered the reason why the earth turns round the sun, and why it does not fly apart." But he was a modest man and kept quiet.

A few years went by. Then one day Newton had a visitor from London. It was Edmund Halley, the astronomer.

"We cannot solve this problem," said Halley. "We need your help. Imagine that gravity works by the law of inverse square. What is the path of a planet in going round the sun?"

"An ellipse," promptly answered Newton.

Halley was taken aback by Newton's readiness. "Why, how do you know?" he gasped.

"I've calculated it."

"Show me your papers."

Newton went to his desk, but was unable to find the papers. He had thrown them away. But he reworked the figures for Halley and in addition showed him all that he had written on science. Halley was lost in admiration.

"These are the greatest discoveries ever made," said he. "I shall have the Royal Society publish them."

The Royal Society, however, had spent its last farthing on printing a book on fish, so that Halley had to publish Newton's *Philosophiae Naturalis Principia Mathematica,* or *Principia* as it is usually called, at his own expense.

Newton's laws of motion are among our finest tools in science. They help explain many phenomena in nature; for example, why there are tides, and how much matter there is in the stars.

IV

Isaac Newton was a mild, pleasant person. Most of his life he was very poor because he gave away his money to whoever needed it more than he. He found plenty of relatives who needed his money. This open-handed charity embarrassed him, for there was a time when he could not afford to pay his dues of one shilling to the Royal Society. The Society, of course, excused him.

He worked so steadily that he scarcely remembered to eat, and begrudged himself his four or five hours of sleep. His modesty, in fact, was exasperating to the scientists of the Royal Society, who waited eagerly for a word from him. They knew that he would not publish his discoveries; he was too busy to say anything about them.

"Dear Mr. Newton," the Society would write. "Have you any findings to tell us about?" As likely as not, he would forget to answer the letter.

Once Newton invited a friend to dinner. The guest arrived; dinner was served. Newton was in his room working. The friend waited some time and then, partly from sheer annoyance, partly from a desire to be smart, ate all the dinner, Newton's share included. Presently the host entered, greeted his friend, and sat down at the table. He lifted the cover of the chief dish, stared awhile blankly at the bone, then said, "I forgot that we have already dined."

His carelessness and absentmindedness were only about himself, never about other people or about his responsibilities. For instance, the English government thought that as its best scientist he should have more time and more money for his researches. They therefore appointed him to a position they intended to be a sinecure, Master of the Mint. Newton, however, took his duties more seriously than the government intended. The result was that he neglected his scientific work, but the mint became more efficient than it had ever been before.

At this time it was the entertaining custom for mathematicians to challenge each other to mathematical duels. In these Newton was never beaten.

In June 1696, John Bernoulli, a famous mathematician, announced two problems and challenged all Europe to solve them within six months. The six months passed, and no one had yet solved the problems, so Bernoulli agreed to extend the time until the next Christmas.

On the evening of the twenty-ninth of January, 1697, Newton came home from a hard day at the mint and found waiting for him a copy of the magazine containing the problems. At once he began work on them, eight months after everybody else. The following morning he gave the solutions to the President of the Royal Society.

V

When Newton peered through one of Galileo's telescopes, he thought about the blurred lens. Poor Galileo had probably lost his sight by straining through the murky glass. "The trouble," Newton believed, "would be overcome if we knew more about light."

He had noticed the beautiful iridescent shades that play in a bubble of soap, or in the glass prisms of the chandelier, and he must have gazed long at a rainbow. He suspected that ordinary white light was not a simple affair after all, and he began to experiment.

He made his room totally dark except for a tiny hole in the window shutter. Through that hole one beam of sunlight streamed into the darkened room and fell upon the opposite wall. Then, in the path of the sunbeam, Newton put a glass prism so that the light went through it. A wonderful thing happened! There on the wall, instead of the round spot of white light, Newton saw a band of seven colors: red, orange, yellow, green, blue, indigo, and violet — the colors of the spectrum, as we now call it.

"Sunlight," he announced, "is a combination of the seven colors of the spectrum. When we say, for instance, that grass is green, the truth is that grass reflects only the green light of the sun's rays. The other six colors it absorbs."

Now he understood why Galileo's telescope blurred the image of the celestial bodies upon which it was focused: the lens acted like a prism; it broke up the light. Galileo's telescope was the refracting kind; that is, it caught the light beam and bent it into the tube. To correct the defect of its lens, Isaac Newton invented another kind of telescope: the reflecting kind. In the Newtonian or reflecting telescope there is no object lens. The light beam enters an open tube and strikes a mirror shaped like a dish. The mirror reflects the beam to a smaller mirror which in turn bounces it into a magnifying eyepiece. It was with the Newtonian telescope that a hundred years later great discoveries were made.

The scientific world considers Isaac Newton one of its greatest heroes.

"If all the geniuses of the universe were assembled," said the French writer Voltaire, "Newton should lead the band."

Alexander Pope, the leading English poet of Newton's day, wrote:

> Nature and Nature's laws lay hid in night;
> God said, "Let Newton be," and all was light.

But Newton himself was modest to the last. "I do not know what I may appear to the world," he said, "but to myself I seem to have been only like a boy playing on the seashore, and diverting myself in now and then finding a smoother pebble or a prettier shell than ordinary, whilst the great ocean of truth lay all undiscovered before me."

Antoine Laurent Lavoisier

(1743–1794)

FOUNDER OF CHEMISTRY

I

AT THE TIME the American colonists were growing indignant over King George's tyranny and the citizens of France were clenching bony fists at their fat king, Louis XVI, there took place daily in the Royal Garden of Paris a lecture in science. Let us attend one of them.

The ladies and gentlemen of the audience are the social best of Paris. Also attending are scientists, doctors, teachers, priests, and students. On the lecture platform Professor Bourdelin stands nervously. In monotonous tones he is explaining an idea in science. His audience, however, seems to be giving him scant attention. The lace bosoms of the men rustle, their silver shoe buckles clink, and the powdered curls of the ladies toss impatiently.

One person, at least, is listening. He is seated as near as possible to the professor and, notebook in hand, is intent upon every word. It is Antoine Laurent Lavoisier, a young law student, who is neglecting his law books in pursuit of his greater love, science. The handsome youth is known to most of the fashionable group, for he comes of a rich family; so rich, in fact, that his house has glass windows. They say of young Lavoisier that he is an excellent student. Did he not win a prize in literary composition? It is rumored even that he is writing a play, but some say that his interest is really in music and painting. Everybody agrees, however, that he is charming.

"Everything that burns," Professor Bourdelin drones on, "does so because it has particles of fire in it. When wood burns, for instance, its fire particles rush out and leave an ash. That proves that wood is made of fire particles plus ashes. Stone cannot burn. Why not? Because it contains no fire particles."

Here and there a yawn is stifled. Presently the professor concludes his lecture: "The demonstrator will now prove all this to you." The professor never soils his hands by performing an experiment. A demonstrator does that. Now Professor Bourdelin retires, much to the relief of his audience.

"How tiresome! Ah, here is Guillaume Rouelle . . . Master Rouelle is here at last."

Applause ripples through the audience. Every eye is on the platform, where now stands a striking figure in velvet breeches and coat, with carefully powdered wig, and a small tricornered hat under his left arm.

"You have all heard from my esteemed colleague," begins Rouelle in a calm, deep voice, "about fire particles that rush out of burning bodies." He pauses, and puts down his hat. "We shall see."

He turns to the long table on which flasks, retorts,

and other pieces of chemical apparatus have been placed. From the table he picks up a glass dish containing a reddish powder.

"Last week, you remember, I heated mercury, a glistening silvery liquid. What happened? You saw that fire sparks, or as we chemists call it, phlogiston, was driven out of the mercury, which as a consequence was changed into this powder we call the calx of mercury."

He gives the glass dish to his assistant. Off comes Rouelle's wig, which he hangs carelessly on the nearest chemical apparatus within reach.

"Today I shall put phlogiston back into the powdery calx of mercury." He heaps granulated charcoal into the dish, completely covering the red powder.

"Light it, young man," he orders his assistant as he unties his cravat. The assistant places it on a large metal pan, so that the flame will not spread beyond the dish. As the charcoal is lighted, its sparks rapidly grow into flames which envelop the container. Rouelle flings his velvet coat from him, and he gesticulates wildly.

"You see," he turns to his audience, "charcoal is rich in fire sparks. From the charcoal's flames the phlogiston returns into the mercury calx. All that is left of the charcoal will be some ashes, but the mercury will be regenerated into the original silvery liquid."

Rouelle's final words to the audience are, "Remember, phlogiston is everywhere, even in you. Every time you breathe, you exhale some phlogiston."

The demonstration is over. The audience applauds Master Rouelle's triumphant lecture.

As young Lavoisier leaves the Royal Garden, he wonders about the phlogiston theory. It sounds convincing enough. But perhaps the explanation is too glib. It occurs to Antoine Lavoisier that it might be possible to weigh each one of the materials that Rouelle used. Could one then prove by the actual weights that phlogiston did enter or leave a chemical?

This question stays with him. In good time young Lavoisier will overthrow the chemical theory of his day and revolutionize the study of chemistry.

II

Several years went by, years of close study for Lavoisier. His brilliance as a scientist was gaining him fame. Already he had been given a prize for an essay on the best way to light Paris at night. The question why things burn was interesting him.

He worked hard. The day was not long enough for him, and he begrudged the time he spent eating. So he put himself on a milk diet. At this, his friends and family protested.

"Dear mathematician," they said, "an additional year on earth, even if you accomplish less, will be of more value to you than the gratitude of mankind for your sacrifice."

Lavoisier did not agree. His zeal for the public welfare was too great. At this time Paris was suffering for lack of suitable drinking water. The young scientist was ready with a plan to pump in the excellent waters of the river Yvette. He also suggested a scheme for setting in hydrants against a fire. Unfortunately there was no money to carry out these measures. But the reward for his brilliant plans came to Lavoisier: the honor of

membership in the Academy of Science was conferred
on him when he was half as old as his fellow members.

Lavoisier was not satisfied with the method of experimenting in those days. It was not precise enough, he
felt. There were not enough instruments and apparatus for weighing and measuring.

"How can we know what happens to things when
they burn," he thought, "if we have no means of careful measuring? We must burn many substances in
many ways . . . I must have machinery. This hit-and-
miss guessing leads nowhere."

To carry out his plans he needed a great deal of
money; and the only way he could get money was by
going into business. The government of France at that
time "farmed" its taxes rather than collecting them directly, and Lavoisier became a farmer-general — one
of a group of men who bought from the king the privilege of levying and collecting taxes. The people of
France hated the farmers-general, who were in many
cases dishonest politicians out to rob them. As a result
Lavoisier was looked upon with suspicion. It was expected that he would let the extortion of money from
the poor go on, and take his share of the loot.

But Lavoisier was the soul of honesty. Like Newton
at the mint, he took his business seriously. Often he
tried to reduce the taxes of the poor, rather than raise
them for his own benefit. Though his scientific work
was the dearest thing in the world to him, he was never
too busy to seek remedies for bettering the lot of the
poor. He was deeply pained, for instance, when he visited the hospitals and prisons and observed the squalid
conditions there. From that time on, he continually

used his influence to secure decent treatment for the inmates.

"If it is possible to make exception in the case of taxes," he said warmly, "it can only be in favor of the poor." And in 1788, when he had amassed a fortune, and the people of Blois and its vicinity were suffering from a severe famine, he donated £50,000 for their relief, of which they took only £38,000. This sum they later offered to return, but he refused to accept it.

He established in 1778 a model farm in Blois at his own expense, in order to prove that if farmers would only apply scientific methods to their lands, the country would become more prosperous. The venture turned out so successfully and the suffering around Blois was alleviated to such an extent that to this day in that community they speak of Lavoisier as their benefactor.

The interest in this first model farm was widespread. George Washington watched it carefully from across the ocean. When Franklin visited France, he made a friend of Lavoisier. Indeed, the success of his experiment was so signal that it led to the establishment in 1785 of the King's Committee on Agriculture, and in 1788 to an assembly for the betterment of the poor. A member of this assembly wrote, "It is Lavoisier who does everything. His name is heard every moment."

One more remarkable piece of public work the world owes to him. Through his efforts there was started in France a Bureau of Life Insurance and Old Age Pensions, which gave the peasant an opportunity to invest small sums of money in such a way that he was assured a settled income in old age.

III

Lavoisier repeated the fire-particle experiment he had seen Rouelle do. But he was much more decisive about it. He burned a piece of tin in a closed vase. Before the burning began, he noted the weight of the tin and the weight of the vase. When the burning or combustion was over, the ashes of the tin weighed more than had the tin itself.

"Where does this added weight come from?" pondered the chemist.

Chemists in those days never asked questions like that. If someone had propounded it, they probably would have said, "If tin weighs more after combustion than before — well, that's the nature of tin." But such an answer did not satisfy Lavoisier.

"The tin gets its added weight somewhere," he insisted. "You can't make something out of nothing. If my tin, vase, and air within the vase, weigh ten pounds altogether before the tin burns, they should weigh the same after." He found this to be true.

"Now," he went on, "if the vase weighs the same after the burning and the tin more, the air must weigh less. The air has given something to the tin."

He noticed that after the burning, the air in the closed vase was unbreathable. "The pure air has joined with the tin." He was sure of it. "What is left of the air is another gas which we cannot breathe. Air must be a mixture of several gases."

He remembered that the English chemist Joseph Priestley had told him of a certain gas in the air which, when he had breathed it, made him feel very lively. "There is a gas in the atmosphere," concluded Lavoisier, "which helps things to burn. In fact, without it there could be no burning, there could be no heat. Maybe we have heat in our bodies because we breathe that gas."

He continued his experiments with burning things. He noticed one more curious fact: that whenever he burned up sulphur, he always found an acid in his dish.

"The gas in the atmosphere — this pure air — has power to form an acid." So he called this gas by the Greek word meaning "acid-former" — oxygen.

The telling blow against the "phlogiston theory" was dealt when Lavoisier repeated the experiment that Rouelle had done with mercury. At every state of the experiment he weighed and reweighed the materials. The result was that he proved to every scientist's satisfaction that there was no such thing as phlogiston, that burning was a fusing of the oxygen of the air with something else.

The interesting discovery was now made by an English chemist, Henry Cavendish, that there is a gas which burns. In his laboratory in Paris Lavoisier manufactured this inflammable gas, and on adding oxygen to it he found that water was formed. The "water-former," or hydrogen, he called this gas discovered by Cavendish.

"Water is no longer the simple liquid it has been supposed," announced Lavoisier. "It is a compound of two gases, hydrogen and oxygen." A glass of water, he further proved, weighs as much as the hydrogen in it, plus the oxygen.

This sort of experimenting brought about a revolution in the practice of chemistry. Lavoisier had made an exact science of it. He discovered new chemical elements in nature and wrote *Elements of Chemistry*, earning for himself the title Founder of Modern Chemistry.

Now it occurred to Lavoisier that the human body must be a great chemical factory. "We inhale oxygen," he reasoned. "That starts heat in the body which keeps life going . . ."

Here the great chemist was interrupted.

IV

The French Revolution had struck. The starving people of Paris, marching to the royal palace, had forced the king to yield to their will. "Bread!" was their cry.

Lavoisier was enthusiastic. "A government," he believed, "is created to make all its people happy, not a small number only. It is a government for everybody."

"There are a few autocrats," he wrote to his friend Benjamin Franklin, "who want to go back to the old system of monarchy. But the best French thinkers are democratic."

In this crisis, France looked to its geniuses to help it. The people made Lavoisier head of the National Treasury. For this work he refused to take a salary. "I have enough for my wants," he said. "Just now, when France needs all its resources, I cannot consent to profit by her trouble."

The king, knowing Lavoisier's skill in financial matters, offered to make him his Minister of Finance. Since the nomination came from the king, he refused. "I have sworn allegiance to the will of the people," said Lavoisier firmly.

Everything he turned to came out the better for his attention. As head of the National Treasury, he improved the system of coinage. He invented the decimal system of coins. It was found to be simple, and is in use today. But a much greater public work was a new system of weights and measures, the metric system, which he and other scientists developed. Almost all nations and scientists throughout the world use it today. Before Lavoisier's time, nearly every province in France had a different system of measurement, so that a merchant from Bordeaux, if he was buying in Lyons, scarcely knew whether he was getting a bargain or paying too much. The business world, as well as the scientific, owes Lavoisier a debt of gratitude.

The greatest public work of Lavoisier, however, was done when he was a member of the Committee on Education. First of all, he believed in free schools. "It is our duty," said he, "to provide education for children."

Then he outlined an entirely new course of study, the industrial arts course. "Academic studies are not enough to offer to our children," he asserted. "We must also teach practical work."

He began his work of revising the entire school program of France, from the first grade up through the universities, but suddenly the guillotine began to rumble in the streets of Paris.

The king and queen were among the first victims. It

was considered a crime to have more than enough
bread to eat in the house, and the heads of all who were
not starving sat weakly on their shoulders. Fifty times a
day the ax fell, to the tune of the "Marseillaise."
Terror reigned.

All at once the cry arose, "The farmers-general!
Those leeches who have sucked the blood of the Republic!"

Warrants were drawn up for the arrest of all the
farmers-general. The charity, the public work, the genius of Lavoisier were forgotten. The same legal paper
that had done for four thousand other wretches served
him, too.

It meant death. Lavoisier's friends urged him to flee.
But the conscience of the scientist was clear and he did
not wait for his arrest; he gave himself up.

Scientists the world over were horrified. They peti-
tioned the judge to save him from death.

"The Republic," was the amazing reply of the judge,
"has no need of scholars."

Lavoisier took his fate calmly. "I have lived a useful
life," he said, "and I am ready."

On the eighth of May, 1794, this hero, who had made
all the civilized world his debtor to the end of time, was
led to the scaffold. Not a murmur disturbed his lips as
he bowed his head on the guillotine. The ax fell.

"It required but a moment," wrote his fellow scientist Joseph Lagrange, "to cut off a head the like of
which one hundred years may not produce."

James Watt

(1736–1819)

"AT THE HEAD OF ALL INVENTORS,
IN ALL AGES AND NATIONS"

I

ONE winter day an English lord was being guided through the madhouse in Paris. As he gazed at the walls about him, his spare old frame shuddering at the human misery there contained, he suddenly heard a hoarse shrieking: "I am not mad! I am not mad! I have made a discovery . . . a discovery . . ."

"What has he discovered?" asked the nobleman anxiously.

"Oh," the guide answered, shrugging his shoulders, "something trifling enough. You would never guess it; he thinks he has found a use for the steam of boiling water . . . To listen to him, you would imagine that with steam you could navigate ships, move carriages, and perform other miracles. He has even written a book on the subject."

That was in 1641.

About one hundred years later in Glasgow, Scotland, one evening a lad of thirteen and his aunt were seated at the tea table. They were silent for some time, until at last the aunt exclaimed impatiently, "James Watt, I

never saw such an idle boy! For the last hour you have
not spoken one word or done one thing but take the
kettle off the fire and put it on again, holding now a
cup and now a silver spoon over the steam, watching
how the steam rises from the spout, and catching and
collecting the steam as it forms into drops of hot water.
Are you not ashamed of spending your time in this
way?"

To a man in Paris the fascination of steaming water
brought madness; to a small Scotch boy, thoughtful-
ness. The madness destroyed the man; the thoughtful-
ness made the lad illustrious.

In his father's carpentry shop, they said of Jamie
Watt that he had "a fortune at his fingers' ends," for he
could wield tools more shrewdly than a skilled mechanic. Although he was too frail to sport with other
boys, the knowledge that he gleaned from books, as he
lay at home on the hearthstone, and the skill at his fingers' ends, enabled him to play in his own way. One
evidence of this was a little electric machine which he
built and with which he startled his friends with electric shocks.

His father's workshop was for him a realm of constant pleasure and surprise. Days were always delightful at the craftsman's bench. There Jamie had a small
forge for his own use, and all he needed for his work
was a supply of odd pieces of metal. A large silver coin,
for instance, if it were shaped and drilled properly,
made a fine ladle, and ladles were useful.

In his house there were several portraits on the walls.
One was of an amusing man in a wig. "Who is that?"
asked Jamie.

"Sir Isaac Newton, lad," answered his father, "one of our greatest men. Come, let me show you."

Leading Jamie into the workshop, he rummaged about until he brought forth a long tube with a glass at either end. "A telescope," he called it, and told Jamie that the stars and the sun and moon are bigger than they seem, bigger even than a large lantern . . .

In the still nights that followed, a small boy lay for hours on his back under the dark, murmuring trees, with a tube held up to his eye.

He would have lived happily enough despite illness, with his books on literature, botany, anatomy, and natural science, had not his mother, the mainstay of his early years, suddenly died. His home was broken up. His father, who had never been rich, now fell upon such hard times that he could not even support his son. Jamie, not yet fourteen and weak in body, went to Glasgow to make his way however he could.

And a meager enough way it was. He became apprentice to an instrument maker, and soon it was said that Watt's compasses and sectors were the best in the field. In his strong desire to learn everything about his trade, however, and keep up his studies at night in his garret, he overstrained and fell dangerously ill.

He recovered, only to find himself out of a job. His talent, though, was known. A professor of science in the University of Glasgow, having seen a sample of Watt's work, offered him a room in the University building, gave him some work to do, and urged him to make and sell instruments. Jamie Watt was happy. In his workshop the professors would gather, and as Jamie worked, they chatted about chemistry, mathematics, mechanics.

They all liked the quiet youth who, in the midst of all their learned talk, kept modestly at his work. When they discovered with amazement that this same modest young man was their equal in learning and even their superior, their admiration and respect for him became immeasurable.

He was so studious, so thorough; his knowledge of science, which he got alone from books, amazed even the best of university students. Someone, for instance, came to ask him to repair an organ. He did not decline because he had never repaired one. He took to studying not only the mechanism of the organ but of the whole range of musical instruments. He solved musical problems that troubled the greatest scientists in Europe. Violins, cellos, organs, guitars, flutes were produced by him. He invented many devices for the organ. From all sides work poured into his little shop.

Yet the vision of the steaming kettle still fired his imagination.

There was in existence a machine called the Newcomen engine. It was used to pump water from collieries and mines. It worked by steam, but was so dangerous and inefficient that it was of little use. Watt examined it, and to himself put the question, "How does it work, and can it be improved?"

He carefully studied the Newcomen engine. He found that it worked as follows. Steam from a boiler was sent into a cylinder. The steam expanded. It then pressed up and, aided by a counterweight, raised the cylinder, to which was attached a beam. To cause the cylinder to drop down again, cold water was jetted on it. The steam was thus cooled and condensed into water again. Then, since there was no more steam to press upon the cylinder, the cylinder fell down and so did the beam. Then the water had to be let out of the cold cylinder and steam sent into it again. In this way, the beam was caused to move up and down and do work.

This was a slow process. The trouble was that in the condensation process the cylinder was cooled so that when the next charge of steam was introduced, four-fifths of the charge went into again heating the cylinder, and only one-fifth of the steam moved the beam.

"If only the cylinder could be kept always hot!" thought Watt.

He was walking in the country one day, pondering over this obstacle, when suddenly the solution flashed into his mind: a separate chamber where the jet of cold water could condense the steam, leaving the cylinder always hot! Home he rushed. He borrowed a syringe, found a tin can, and set about making a model of a new steam engine.

He rented a cellar, and for six months labored over his model. In order to study the subject thoroughly, he learned new languages — German, French, and Italian, because there were books on engines in those tongues that he ought to read. But he did not rely on books alone. He was too good a scientist to do that. Since he was studying the nature of steam, he made clouds of it in his shop. He compressed it into small bottles, he let it expand in big ones. He watched steam behave in all sorts of ways, and discovered things about it that no other scientist knew. At length he was ready to build his engine.

A new era had dawned — the age of steam. Even at

the beginning of its career the new engine was a hundred times more efficient than the old. It did not matter what the work was, the steam engine could do it — it could pull, drive, turn, hammer, shape. It took over the brutal, backbreaking labor of the men in the factories. It powered the two great new methods of transportation on land and sea — the locomotive and the steamship.

II

There are few days so illustrious in history as the fifth of January, 1769. It was indeed a happy day for the human toiler, for on that day James Watt received his patent on the steam engine.

His troubles were far from over. They had, in fact, just begun. Ideas for steamboats and locomotives were straining in his mind, but he had no time to let them out. To manufacture engines requires money; to continue study and experiment, more money. So he had to work as a surveyor and engineer to support himself.

Like Lavoisier, he solved the water problem for a city, the city of Glasgow. And throughout his daily labors, his mind teemed with other scientific ideas and inventions.

At last, by 1776, his engine was acclaimed by everybody. The eyes of the world were upon him, and he could call himself successful. At the height of his powers now, he gave shape to all his schemes. Inventions of all kinds came from him in profusion: a drying machine, a new micrometer, a new surveying quadrant, a drawing mashine, a copying press for sculpture, astronomical instruments — these are only a few of his gifts to humanity.

"Gimcracks!" he called them modestly, and so fast did he turn them out that one of his friends once greeted him by saying, "I daresay you have invented, since I saw you, five hundred engines."

There was a club in Birmingham called the Lunar Society whose members discussed every conceivable subject. The center of attraction was Watt, for everything in the book of nature and man was his study. To his friend Sir Walter Scott, he talked about the writing of novels. To a friend who was a student of languages, he talked of the origins of the alphabet. He could advise an artist on the best hair for brushes, or a musician on playing a dulcimer. His mind, like his steam engine, could do anything.

His favorite science was chemistry, and as a chemist he was one of the best of his time. When he was in Paris, he visited Lavoisier, with whom he found he had an unexpected bond. Before the two scientists met, each had discovered, unknown to the other, that water was composed of two gases. That fact must have made the two chemists great friends.

Every learned society in Europe paid him tribute; every academy honored itself by electing him a member. The governments of Russia and France both offered him handsome posts, if he would only consent to live in their countries. For a while, English scientists were alarmed lest they lose him. He stayed, however, in Scotland.

The heart beats faster to think of him as an old man, still working in a garret to lighten the labors of men; a kindly old man, unassuming and generous, ready to encourage any young person applying to him, conversing with equal knowledge on every subject conceivable — languages and literature, science, medicine, law, music — and with a modest courtesy that has made him one of the most beloved characters history has known.

His work was done. On August 19, 1819, he left the world richer a millionfold than when he entered it. The world's tribute to James Watt is expressed in a colossal statue of him in Westminster Abbey which bears the inscription:

Not to Perpetuate a Name
Which must endure while the Peaceful Arts flourish
But to shew
That Mankind have learnt to honour those
Who best deserve their Gratitude
The King
His Ministers and Many of the Nobles
And Commoners of the Realm
Raised a Monument to
JAMES WATT
Who directing the force of an Original Genius
Early exercised in Philosophic Research
To the Improvement of
The Steam Engine
Enlarged the Resources of his Country
Increased the Power of Man
And rose to an Eminent Place
Among the Most Illustrious Followers of Science
And the Real Benefactors of the World
Born at Greenock MDCCXXXVI
Died at Heathfield in Staffordshire MDCCCXIX

Humphry Davy

(1778–1829)

THE POET-CHEMIST

I

SOMETHING over one hundred years ago families in the mining regions of England were in a state of terror and anguish. The bitter wail of mother and child was striking to the heart of the world, as almost daily the shattered bodies of their menfolk were brought home to them. From every mine and colliery, the news of disaster upon fresh disaster stunned and halted the progress of civilization; and the bereaved ones, thrown into dire poverty, became everybody's concern. The explosions in the coal mines, it seemed, could not be checked, and miners seemed doomed to annihilation.

On May 25, 1812, ninety-two men and boys were killed by an explosion in a mine. In another mine eighteen months later, twenty-three were killed. Over a year later fifty-seven more were mangled to death. Then again the same number, and this list of tragedies was being repeated in all mining regions of England. The country was in despair. Many mines were shut and it seemed as though industry itself was about to die.

The mine owners, in the summer of 1815, decided to

appeal to Humphry Davy, who at thirty-seven was the greatest living chemist. The Welsh chemist was then traveling in England and the appeal was made to him by letter. Davy was informed that in the depths of mines there lurked a malignant gas which caught fire from the miners' candles and exploded. Could anything be done about it?

Very shortly after the letter to Davy was sent, Mr. Buddle, a mine owner of Bristol, was brooding anxiously in the office of his Wallsend colliery when two visitors were announced. One was the Bishop of Bristol, who presented Mr. Buddle to his pleasant-faced young companion.

"Mr. Davy," he said.

But Mr. Buddle was by no means overcome with joy. On the contrary his gloom continued. He did not see that anything could be done to relieve the tragic plight of the miners.

"You see, sir," he explained, "wherever we mine coal, gas gushes out of the coal bed. That situation is critical, for the gas is explosive and we miners must have light to do our work. We must use light," he repeated. "Unfortunately gas pervades the mines. It is hopeless."

Humphry Davy listened thoughtfully. Then he began to question Mr. Buddle carefully on the exact working conditions in the mines, the nature of the gas, how it hissed from the breaks in the rock, and whether or not he could take back with him samples of the gas. On being assured that he could, he arose, and looking keenly at the dejected mine owner, said, "I think I can do something for you."

Mr. Buddle glanced up incredulously. Davy, however, smiled. "Do not despair," he said kindly. "I think I can do something for you in a very short time."

Two weeks passed. Then one day a package came from London to Mr. Buddle. It contained a new sort of lamp and a letter from Davy.

"I flatter myself," wrote the chemist, "that this lamp I have invented will answer your purpose. Try it."

Mr. Buddle was skeptical. He was also desperate. Calling together a few of his miners and showing them the lamp, he bade them prepare for a descent into the mine.

"Surely, sir," protested one of the men, pointing with contempt at Davy's lamp, "this will not save us from being blown to pieces." And a chorus of voices took up the protest.

"Nevertheless," said Mr. Buddle firmly, "we will test the lamp, danger or no danger. I shall lead the way."

By this time, the wives of the miners had collected, and their lament and wailing were so great that it was only by physical force that they could be kept off. At last the men were lowered into the pit of the mine where they expected to meet with instantaneous destruction. Indeed, their dread was so great that the slightest noise terrified them. Suddenly the hiss of the gas was heard.

"Let us go back!" the men implored. But even as they spoke, the gas swept over the flame of the lamp. It swept over . . . and the flame but burned the brighter for it.

On went the little party, carrying their lamp high like a banner, with new courage in their hearts.

"The monster is destroyed," said Mr. Buddle exultingly. "The Davy has saved us."

The name stuck. From then on, a man would not
think of going into a mine without his "Davy."

Some time later, Humphry Davy himself visited Mr.
Buddle again.

The mine owner tried to express to the scientist the
gratitude and the jubilation that the world felt.

"But, Mr. Davy," he wondered, "is it not remarkable
that so simple an instrument can defy an enemy hereto-
fore unconquerable?"

Davy laughed. "It is simple," he agreed. "But it
serves. When I examined the samples of the gas, or firedamp, I found that the gas exploded violently only
when it mixed with a great deal of air — seven times its
own amount, in fact. It burns by the help of the oxygen
in the air. So, by uniting with the oxygen and thus taking it from the air, it makes the air unbreathable.
Then, to add to the danger, it explodes. In this way, I
saw that air and firedamp should be kept away from
each other. The first thing I had to do, therefore, was to
make it impossible for much air to enter my lamp —
though I needed some air, because, as Lavoisier
showed, a flame will not burn without the oxygen of
the air. I finally hit on the idea of allowing the air to
enter only by all these very small tubes you see. By this
means, only the meager amount of air that the flame
needs can enter.

"Besides, I further discovered that the gas explodes
only when it is very hot. I was afraid that if, by accident, enough air and gas did combine, the metal sides
of my lamp would be hot enough to set fire to the mix-

ture. So I had to think of a way to draw off some of the heat from the metal of the lamp. Do you see all the wire gauze around the flame? That gauze uses up part of the heat, so that the sides of the lamp can never grow hot enough for the gas to explode. Yes, it is a simple instrument."

As a token of their gratitude, the mine owners presented Davy with a dinner service of silver plate worth about six thousand dollars. In his will he stipulated that the silver should be melted and sold, and the proceeds be devoted to founding a medal to be given annually for the most important discovery in chemistry. The Emperor of Russia sent Davy a vase; and the King of England shortly after conferred on him the title of baronet.

A friend of Davy's urged him to patent his lamp, and make money out of it.

"My good friend," replied Davy, "my sole object was to serve humanity, and if I have succeeded, I am amply rewarded. I have never received so much pleasure from any other of my chemical labors, for I trust the cause of humanity will gain something by it."

Like Lavoisier, Davy was the friend of mankind. Even before he invented his safety lamp, the name of Davy was known in the scientific and social world. But afterwards, in every cottage, however humble, the name of Sir Humphry Davy was like a charm.

II

The rise of Davy was all the more brilliant in that he had not had much schooling. At the age of seventeen he was apprentice to a surgeon and apothecary. The strange liquids and powders about him in the laboratory fascinated him so much that he would take them to his garret and there mix them, burn them, taste them, shake them, do this and that, and generally alarm his mother with the rich smells and sudden sizzlings. His sister's dresses showed the effects of his experiments, and his mother was warned that he would some day blow her and everybody around to shreds.

But he was not playing idly in his experiments. Lavoisier's *Elements of Chemistry* was his constant guide. So skillful a chemist did the lad become, in fact, that Dr. Beddoes heard of his talents and engaged him as superintendent of his hospital in Bristol.

There the young chemist became interested in gases of all kinds. He thought patients could perhaps be cured by inhaling the proper gases, if he could only discover them. In his small laboratory, he was constantly risking his life by inhaling various gases that he manufactured. On one occasion he was found unconscious, and with great difficulty brought back to life.

One day, after he had breathed quantities of a peculiar gas which he had just discovered, his friends were amazed at a certain change in him. For no apparent reason, he began to dance. And dancing, he began to laugh hilariously. He could not control the gales of laughter that shook him, until he suddenly subsided and fell into a long deep sleep. Davy had discovered nitrous oxide, or laughing gas, which was later to become so useful in dentistry.

His fame spread abroad. Encouraged by his success, he became interested in the general questions of science. For instance, despite Lavoisier's proof to the contrary, it was still widely believed that fire or heat was a distinct substance like wood or stone. "Wood burns," it was agreed, "because it has in it a fire substance which rushes out."

Of course all scientists did not believe this. Count Rumford, for one, in his lectures at the Royal Institution in London, said that heat was not a distinct substance. "It is known," thought Count Rumford, "that amber when rubbed becomes magnetic. With heat, it is the same way. When the swarms of tiny steel particles are excited, the steel grows hot. We cannot, with our eyes, see the specks of steel dancing about heatedly, but it is surely the dancing which makes the steel hot."

In Bristol, Davy heard of the Count's idea, and it seemed reasonable to him. But how could it be tested? Like a good scientist Davy always looked for the test. One day it came to him. In freezing weather he took two pieces of ice and began rubbing them together. The result was victory; instead of ice, he soon had a small pool of water.

Elated by this proof that rubbing or exciting the bits of ice will heat them and melt them, he wrote to the Count about it. The gratified answer came shortly, and with it — it took the youth's breath away! — an engagement to lecture at the great Royal Institution at London, and Davy only twenty-two years old!

But he was as brilliant as he was young. For twelve years he remained with the Institution, amazing the scientific world with one discovery after another. He seemed to be capable of anything. No matter what the nature of the chemical mystery, Davy could clear it up.

He was required by the Institution, for instance, to lecture on agriculture. "I know nothing about it," objected Davy. Nevertheless, he was ordered to try. With study, he soon became its greatest living authority, and published a book on the chemistry of agriculture.

The city of London was so amazed at the natural wonders of chemistry as Davy showed them at the Royal Institution, and so smitten with the charm of the young scientist, that it became fashionable for the ladies and gentlemen of London society to frequent Davy's lectures as they might a theatre.

One morning, when they had assembled in the lecture hall, they noticed Davy and his assistant, Michael Faraday, busy with a boxlike apparatus on the table. Wonderingly, they looked at it. What could it be? Suddenly Davy nodded to his assistant, who touched something. The audience gasped and stared with open mouths at a chain of white light that had burst from the box and was crackling brilliantly in the air.

Davy, the magician, stood near the column of light, watching it keenly. "This is the light from electricity," he announced.

He reached under the table and drew out a small magnet with which he began to make passes at the crackling stream of light. The light bent. No matter where Davy held the magnet, thither the light curved, writhing and dancing under Davy's direction.

In this way Davy produced the electric arc light for the first time in history. Today it is a common enough sight because of Edison's invention of the electric bulb, but in those days it seemed like a miracle from heaven.

Davy was delighted with his electric battery. To try

out the effect of electricity on the human body, he used
to send the current through different parts of his own
frame. He was, indeed, very strongly attached to his
battery. When his tongue was attached to it, a sour taste
filled his mouth. When his eye was attached, he saw a
flash of light.

"I feel a shock," he told the members of the Royal
Institution, "then a numbness and a tingling sensation."

One illustrious day, he sent a current of electricity
through two glasses of water. At once, bubbles of two
different gases began to form, and the water to disappear.

"Lavoisier was right," Davy told his audience.
"Water is a compound of two gases — hydrogen and
oxygen. The electric current has broken the liquid up
into its two parts."

"Now," reasoned Davy, "if an electric current can
break water up into its simple elements, it can do the
same to other things." He knew that most things are
like water, in that they consist of several elements
united in one body. A club of men is like that. One
member is a doctor, another a lawyer, and a third a
businessman; they meet and form a club. Just so, water
is a club of two members. And Lavoisier was the great
detective who discovered the members.

Our world is made up of countless clubs of elements,
and Davy determined that with his powerful battery he
would break into as many clubs as he could and find
out who the members are.

He began with a rather homely sort of organization
— potash. He melted the potash in a spoon, and con-

nected the spoon with his battery. At once a beautiful sight appeared. A vivid light glowed at the tip of one wire of his battery, and at another point a column of flame arose. As Davy watched, the liquid potash began to bubble, and in the spoon shone tiny globules. They looked like droplets of quicksilver, but they were not.

"A new element! The tiny globules are a new element!" cried Davy, dancing around like a happy lunatic. "Potassium!" he called the element.

A few days later he discovered sodium in the same way, and in the days following he added four more to the list of elements.

III

"If Davy had not been the first chemist of his day, he would have been the first poet," wrote Samuel Taylor Coleridge, one of our greatest English writers and a friend of Davy. Coleridge attended the great chemist's lectures at the Institution for the sake of hearing the rich metaphors that Davy used with glowing eloquence. Nor was Coleridge the only literary man to admire Davy's poetic talent. Robert Southey, appointed poet laureate of England in 1813, when doubtful of one of his poems, wanted no better criticism than Davy's opinion.

Napoleon Bonaparte offered Davy an honorary prize. England and France were then at war, and many narrow-minded Englishmen spoke to Davy warning him not to accept the prize from the "enemy of his country." But Davy was reasonable and accepted the prize. He, who had saved the lives of the miners of France as well as those of England, said, "If two countries are at war, men of science are not. We should, through men of science, soften national hostility."

Like all our heroes, Davy never ceased working. In his efforts to serve the cause of science, which gives people the good things of the world and an understanding of life, he overworked and fell ill. Death itself he did not fear. But he was always afraid he might die before finishing the experiment on which he was engaged.

In Rome in 1826, paralysis crippled his right side, but he worked on as best he could. Even on the day of his death, May 29, 1829, like Galileo, his last concern was to leave directions for the completion of an important experiment.

Marie Sklodowska Curie

(1867–1934)

A MATTER OF MYSTERY

I

IT IS the year 1200. In a gloomy cell an old man in a skullcap is working feverishly. A smoking crucible is in his hand, and his eyes fairly start from their sockets as he peers into it. Is there a glitter as of gold in the vessel?

All his life he has been looking for that yellow gleam. Some people call him a charlatan. Others revere him as a philosopher. Nothing, however, can shake his faith in the belief that lead can be changed to gold. Only . . . the world is growing tired of waiting, and he himself — unless the elixir of life is soon found — will not need gold.

The actor of this scene is an alchemist, the ancestor of the chemist. He stakes his reputation on the principle that at bottom all things are one and the same, and that therefore lead is the same as gold — if one can find the secret of the shiny disguise.

The scene might serve as a prologue to the greatest drama of the scientific stage — "What are things made of? What is the stuff that we touch and see all about us?" It is the oldest of questions, and every thinker has offered his opinion on it.

"Nonsense!" said some people. "It is a foolish question to ask. You know well enough that water is water, and that air is air. They are not made of anything but themselves."

Then came Lavoisier and showed that water is really a compound of two gases, hydrogen and oxygen, and that air is a mixture of several.

"Very well," was granted grudgingly. "But you can't go any further. Our world is made of hydrogen, oxygen, and a few dozen more elements."

But scientists did try to go further. "What are hydrogen and oxygen and all other elements made of?"

In the year 1880, William Crookes, an English chemist, was wondering what happens when an electric current is sent through a vacuum tube. He knew that a gas, such as air, would not conduct electricity except as a short spark. One day he pumped most of the air out of a glass tube. Through the tube he sent an electric current. To the amazement of Crookes, one end of the tube began to glow with a queer light.

"What causes these rays of light?" wondered Crookes. "And what are the rays made of?"

Idle wonder was useless. He must trick the rays into speaking for themselves. The ruse was simple. Into the tube he put the tiniest, lightest vane. Now as the mysterious rays fell on the vane, they answered one of Crookes's questions by making the little vane pirouette about and grow hot.

"As you see," said the rays in effect, "we are millions

of solid particles streaming ahead with all our might, knocking down everything in our way."

But where do the particles come from and why do they clash about so? There was only one source — the little quantity of air in the tube. But . . .

And there the matter stood.

The next scene in the great mystery takes place fifteen years later in the laboratory of a German professor of physics, Wilhelm Konrad Roentgen. He too is experimenting with sending an electric current through a tube in which is a partial vacuum. He is repeating the experiment of Crookes, but for variation he has thrown a curtain over the tube. The professor's table, by the way, is littered with all sorts of things. "Careless and absentminded!" he is called. But this time it pays to be careless, for in the welter of tubes, chemicals, and papers, there is also a photographer's screen.

The professor starts the current through the covered tube when, for no apparent reason, the plate on the table begins to shine brilliantly. What is the connection? The professor turns off the current in his tube; the glow on the plate subsides. There are some unknown rays, concludes the professor, that can pass through a heavy curtain.

On December 28, 1895, Dr. Roentgen attended a scientific meeting to explain his experiments. "There are powerful rays — let us call them X rays — that can pass through solid matter. With these rays," he announced, "it is possible to see the bones of the hand." The audience snickered. "Anyone volunteer?"

The chairman of the meeting accepted the challenge immediately. "Try me."

The X-ray machine was turned on. The bones in his hand stood out clearly on the plate. The scientists gasped.

"Unbelievable," was the only word they could say to each other as they applauded vigorously.

"What are these rays?" scientists wondered. Everyone began experimenting with electric currents, vacuum tubes, and X rays.

Then came a remarkable discovery by a French scientist. He was studying the effect of uranium salt on photographic plates. He was astonished at the radioactive rays that came from the uranium. The discoverer rushed off to tell his friends Professor and Madame Curie about the great find — and here the heroine enters on the scene of this great scientific drama.

II

Marie Sklodowska was the daughter of a Polish professor of science in Warsaw. Her love for her father and reverence for his calling as a scientist made it a keen joy for her to help him in his laboratory. With the same fascination that she herself was later to inspire in her hearers, she listened daily to his talks with students. Even in the gray days when their poverty was a source of suffering, she lived in the romance of science and saw the magic in chemical adventure. But it was the strange magic of truth, and a romance so real that she never felt the poverty of her home.

Nor did hardship daunt her any the more when she was a grown woman, alone as a student in Paris. Far from home and frequently having to make a meal of bread and milk, she was amply nourished by dreams of becoming a scientist and doing her share for humanity. For a long time she could not get work. Then one day a professor of the University of Paris allowed her to work in his laboratory. It did not occur to him that she was of any value as a scientific worker; the duties he assigned her were those of a caretaker in his laboratory.

Marie was invited one evening to the home of another professor. Upon entering the room, she saw, standing framed by the French window opening on the balcony, a tall young man with auburn hair and large limpid eyes. The professor introduced this young physicist, Pierre Curie, whom he esteemed highly, to Marie Sklodowska. The young scientist spoke to her in a very cordial and sympathetic vein. There was a gentle expression on his face; it seemed to Marie as if he were a dreamer absorbed in his reflection.

They spoke of the possible adventures in science, or of how the world could be made better.

"It would be a lovely thing," said Pierre, after they had known each other for a year, "for us to pass through life together with our dreams: our dreams for humanity, our dreams for science."

That was the beginning of that great partnership of two scientists whose glorious struggles have revealed the most amazing thing in our world since the days of Galileo.

III

When Madame Curie heard from Roentgen of the queer behavior of uranium, she decided to devote herself to the study of it. Her husband, meanwhile, was hard at work on the study of crystals, a work for which he became famous.

Now uranium is taken from an ore called pitchblende. Madame Curie's first task, therefore, was to extract the uranium from a lump of pitchblende. The uranium out, the rest of the ore was supposed to be useless and uninteresting. When Madame Curie had extracted the uranium, however, she made her first discovery — that the pitchblende, supposed to be worthless, still gave off rays.

"There is something startling here!" she told her husband. "This is not what I expected. In the remaining ore some unknown substance must be hidden which has a much greater radioactivity than uranium. If I can only find out what it is!"

At this Pierre Curie could not restrain his excitement and, leaving his crystals, joined his wife on her road of discovery. What causes the radioactivity in the ore? Marie outlined her plan. "We must separate the pitchblende into its elements by chemical means. Test each of the elements with an electroscope for radioactivity. Discard those elements that have no radioactivity. Whatever remains of the ore will be the active portion. Some further chemical analysis, and the task is done."

At the very outset they were handicapped. They needed great quantities of the pitchblende ore. Exactly how much they did not know, for they could not tell where their experiments would lead. Certainly they needed more than they could afford to buy.

The largest mines of pitchblende were at that time

owned by Austria, and the Curies decided to appeal frankly to the Austrian government. Were they not working for common humanity? The Austrian government responded generously with a gift of a ton of the peaty brown ore. They had to pay, however, for transporting it to Paris. The director of the School of Physics in Paris permitted the eager scientists to use a large abandoned shed on the grounds of the college.

The Curies began an exciting search. "This shouldn't take us more than three or four weeks — at the most several months," Marie predicted optimistically.

It was not so at all. Irritating gases from a steaming cauldron filled the air, as they worked with about forty pounds of material at a time. Sometimes she passed the whole day mixing a boiling mass with an iron rod nearly as big as herself. In the evening she was broken with fatigue. On other days the work would be most minute and delicate. In the winter the makeshift laboratory in which they worked was wet and bitter cold. In the summer, because of its glass roof, it was unbearably hot. They might have honestly given up in discouragement, for as time went on, they used up almost all their pitchblende and found only a slight trace of the material they wanted. Nevertheless, in the evening Pierre and Marie would go back to the shed to look at the bottles containing the radioactive products, feebly luminous like faint fairy lights in the dusk.

The weeks became months, and the months stretched to years. Even so, they had many happy moments when they discussed their progress. An unknown force was coming reluctantly out of the pitchblende under the fingers of the searchers. Its rays were more penetrating than anything yet discovered. It revealed the inside of bodies of wood and stone more vividly than they had imagined possible. Polonium they named the new element, in honor of Madame Curie's native country, Poland. "Our long search is ended," they thought. But no! The residue had still greater powers, and the Curies went back to their task of getting to the core of this radiation.

In 1898 a pinch of a grayish white powder, looking like salt, was all the Curies had to show for six tons of pitchblende and four years of work! Yet the small quantity of this powder, one tenth of a gram, was their greatest discovery, a new element — radium. The intensity of the rays that emanate from radium are several million times greater than the rays for uranium.

Some of the rays shot out of radium consist of particles traveling almost with the speed of sunlight — 186,000 miles in one second.

IV

While the Curies were busy exploring the radioactive rays, a physicist, Ernest Rutherford, had been working in England on other radioactive puzzles. For more and more radioactive substances were being discovered.

In 1900 Rutherford had discovered that the element thorium emits a gas which is also radioactive. He wondered, what are these radioactive rays? Are these atoms? Or are they perhaps fragments of atoms? He found that each second a number of the radium atoms become unstable, and disintegrate with extreme violence. His experiments showed that the rays shot out from radioactive elements are not all alike. He identified two of the different types of rays. One type he called alpha, and the second beta.

Rutherford now laid out a large number of experiments for himself. A group of students who were interested in radioactive substances gathered about him. We want to join you in learning more about these rays, they said.

He was happiest when he was working in his laboratory. When things went well, his voice would boom out in song loud enough to be heard throughout the entire laboratory.

As he walked on his daily rounds through his research laboratory, he greeted each research worker cheerfully: How is your experiment coming along? Anything new? Anything unexpected? Any troubles? The two would then discuss that experiment at length.

At tea time, the "team" would congregate in one of the laboratories to relax. "Papa" would sit at the table. His large physique made him look like the teacher with his pupils either perched on stools or sitting on benches close by. From general conversation the team would drift to the scientific projects. How do you explain this? . . . Something must be faulty with the apparatus, because . . .

They all knew that Papa, although most friendly, was an impatient man, always wanting to know the results of each experiment in a hurry. So great was his enthusiasm, however, that the team, too, was infected with his excitement.

Rutherford's experiments showed that the alpha rays are particles that are electrically positive, and that the beta rays are electrically negative. Now he turned to the question: what must the atom be like? . . . How could he account for the rays? He took a bold step. He conceived a model of an atom that was like a miniature solar system. In the center, instead of the sun, was a nucleus which consisted of a group of particles called protons. Tiny electrons, planetlike, whirled around the nucleus in definite paths.

If the electrons are electrically negative particles, he reasoned, then the protons must be positively charged. The two together make the atom electrically neutral. The number of protons in each atom equals the number of electrons. It is easy to picture the path of the single electron of the hydrogen atom, or that of the two electrons of the helium atom, Rutherford explained.

When we examine the elements which have many electrons, the overall arrangement of the paths of the electrons becomes complicated.

It seems that the number of the electrons, and their arrangement, determine both the physical and the chemical properties of the atom. For that reason, the chemical properties of the elements fluorine, chlorine, bromine and iodine are similar because the patterns of the orbits of their electrons are also similar.

Rutherford now turned his attention to the radioactive elements. The Curies found that radium emits powerful radioactive rays, the beta rays. These rays are the electrons of the atom that are in the outer paths of the atom. When the atom loses these, the chemical properties of the atom consequently change.

The radium atom thus breaks down in the process. An electron is ejected, and a new atom is formed, radon. In turn the radon atom is unstable, and soon changes into the atom of another element. More transformations occur until, at last, it becomes a stable, non-radioactive atom, lead.

V

The world hailed Professor and Madame Curie with honors. They were given the Nobel Prize for physics in 1903. Madame Curie was appointed special lecturer at the Sorbonne in Paris, the only woman ever to have had that distinction.

One day a terrible sorrow visited Madame Curie and the world. The former lost her beloved husband; and the latter, a great man. Pierre Curie was the victim of a fatal accident.

The bereft woman still had her work, even though she must now do it alone. In 1911 she was awarded the Nobel Prize again, this time for chemistry.

In the course of her work with radium, she became interested in its healing power. Only one must be very careful in using radium therapy. Pierre Curie was the first to show the danger of it. How? By exposing his arm to it for several hours. The result was a wound for Pierre Curie which took months to heal.

An American who visited Madame Curie was greatly surprised to find her far from rich.

"The money on your patent . . . " she suggested.

"There were no patents," replied Madame Curie quietly. "This would be contrary to the spirit of science. Radium is an element. It belongs to all people." After her husband's death, Madame Curie was usually dressed in black. She had become a solitary woman. Whenever Rutherford met her, he always remarked how pale and ill she looked. She died of pernicious anemia. No wonder. The cells in the marrow of her spine had been destroyed by the radiation with which she worked for over thirty years.

At the time that Madame Curie was continuing with her research on radium, Ernest Rutherford was still experimenting with radioactive rays. "Suppose I use alpha particles from radium C as projectiles," he thought. "With these I'll bombard the atoms of nitrogen gas. If, say, 100,000 alpha particles are shooting in a space where there are nitrogen atoms, certainly a small number of them will collide with some nitrogen atoms. One of my swift projectiles may even hit a nucleus of a nitrogen atom, and disrupt it. That will change the atom into something else, possibly into another element."

Whenever an alpha ray collided with the nucleus of the nitrogen atom, the nucleus disintegrated, and some of the protons were ejected. Hydrogen atoms resulted! Ernest Rutherford had succeeded in deliberately transmuting one element into another. A new science, nuclear chemistry, was born.

The work of the Curies and of Rutherford had opened the nuclear age. In the nuclear civilization, man's ability to transform one element into another, to create new elements, and to build nuclear power plants, should provide us with riches beyond any alchemist's dream.

Albert Einstein

(1879–1955)

THE THEORY OF RELATIVITY

I

THERE were never two men more puzzled than Professors Albert Michelson and Edward Morley in the year 1887.

"There must be a conspiracy of nature against us," they protested.

The cause of their bewilderment was the result of an experiment to determine how fast the earth travels in space. How fast it revolved around the sun they knew already. They also knew the direction in which the entire solar system was moving through the starry heavens. But at what speed? To find the answer to that question the two scientists devised an ingenious apparatus. With it they were confident they could find the answer.

The answer they got seemed ridiculous. If one of their students had asked them why they were puzzled, they might have said: "Think of a swimmer. It takes him a longer time to swim against the current and back than to swim the same distance across the stream and back. Now if we know the speed of the swimmer in still water, we can figure out the rate of the current.

"We have sent a swimmer out in space, but this swimmer was a beam of light. We expected that if a beam of light were sent in the direction the earth travels and then reflected back by a mirror to its starting point, it should take more time than if the beam were sent across the direction the earth travels and back. Instead, we find that it takes a beam of light exactly the same time to go out a certain distance in the direction of the earth's motion and come back as it takes when the beam is directed in any other direction. Whether to the east or to the north — no matter in what direction — always we get the same answer. At all times a beam of light passes an observer at exactly the same speed. How can we account for this?

"Light acts as though the earth were stationary. Must we say that the earth does not move through space?"

That was the dilemma in which Michelson and Morley found themselves. The experiment was repeated, more accurately than before, but with the same result: the earth was stationary! New and even more ingenious experiments of different kinds were tried. Again the same result. Was nature playing a game, in one breath telling us of our motion through space, in the next denying it?

That was the state of affairs until a young scholar named Albert Einstein solved the puzzle. His solution did much more. It changed the science of physics and changed our conception of the universe of which we are a part. Albert Einstein was only twenty-six years old at the time of his discovery. He earned his living as clerk in the patent office at Zurich, Switzerland.

II

He was born in Ulm, Germany on May 14, 1879. He was a quiet, dreamy child, often to be found alone in the garden back of his father's house, humming to himself little songs he composed.

When Albert was five years old his father showed him a compass. The swinging needle awakened in the child a sense of wonder. What caused the needle to act as it did? The wonder grew in him until it embraced the entire realm of nature. To the very end of his days he was occupied with trying to explain electromagnetic forces in the universe.

At school Einstein, like Newton, was an indifferent scholar; at least, his teachers thought him so. The reason may have been that the Munich schools which he attended, like all German schools at that time, were far from pleasant. They were like military establishments where the pupils were army recruits and the teachers were officers to be obeyed without question.

One day Albert heard the word "algebra." It was a curious word, so he asked his uncle, an engineer, what it meant.

"Algebra," said his uncle, "is a lazy man's arithmetic. If you don't know a thing, call it X, and act as if you do know it."

That was fun. Before long, Albert had solved all the problems in an algebra book his father gave him. And when his friends were still grinding on decimals, he was enjoying the beauties of the calculus. His teacher of mathematics declared that the fifteen-year-old boy could easily enter the second year of college.

In 1894, his family moved to northern Italy. For a while, the joys of mathematics yielded to the glories of nature. The rugged peaks of the Apennines, the wild majesty of cliff and mountainside, appealed to the youth. Alone, he wandered about the country. He breathed freely. Liberation from the rigid discipline of the Munich high school, the freshness of Italian landscape, the gaiety of Italian life — all fed his imagination.

For six months he was free of school. At length, however, it was necessary to think about preparing himself for the university. So he went to Switzerland where he enrolled at the Zurich Polytechnic Institute.

Here he no longer was the indifferent scholar of the high school. Already he was showing astonishing originality in mathematics and physics. He hoped to become a teacher and devote himself to undertanding the laws of nature. He was, however, unable to secure immediate appointment as a teacher and, for the time being, earned his living as a clerk in the Swiss patent office. In his spare time he worked on his science and mathematics.

III

Scientists were still bewildered by the Michelson-Morley experiment when suddenly Albert Einstein presented an explanation which burst like a bomb in the midst of our peaceful science, upsetting all our old ideas.

The Michelson-Morley experiment had seemed to show that the earth is apparently standing still; yet we know it is moving around the sun!

Certainly, said Einstein. It is doing both. It all depends on how you look at it. Suppose you were sitting in your cabin on a large ocean liner, gliding smoothly through the water.

As you sit in the cabin, you see your father move about from one part of the room to another. The walls of the room, however, do not move. Only your father moves when he changes his position.

You are reading a book. If you happen to let go of it the book drops straight down at your feet.

Now suppose you step out on deck and then leave the ship. Say you decide to go to a nearby promontory of land. Meanwhile the ship continues on its way. You reach the cliff just as the ship sails by and you get a last glimpse into the cabin. You see your father drop a book. Does it seem to fall straight down this time?

No. The cabin is moving; therefore everything in it is moving, too. The book, as it falls, moves not only downward but forward. Does the book fall straight? Yes and no. It depends on whether you are inside the cabin or on the land looking into the moving cabin.

As Albert Einstein explained it: All nature is in continuous motion. How can we tell? By comparison only. For instance, you cannot discover the motion of the earth unless you compare it — that is, relate it — to some other object in the heavens. Since Professors Michelson and Morley did not so relate it they could not detect the earth's motion.

There is only one incomparable event in nature: a

beam of light. The speed with which light beams travel is the sole and absolute measure of every other event in nature. This means, among other things, that nothing can travel faster than light. Except in science fiction, of course. If you could travel faster than light you would grow younger, like the girl in the limerick:

> *There was a young lady named White*
> *Whose movements were faster than light.*
> *She went out one day*
> *In a relative way*
> *And returned the previous night.*

The only trouble with this prescription for keeping young is that it is impossible.

What the Michelson-Morley experiment showed, therefore, was that light from any source passes us with a speed that is constant, unchanging, regardless of whether we are moving toward its source or away from it.

Einstein also pointed to something which had not been adequately taken into account by our science. One had always supposed that objects had only three dimensions — length, width and height. But there is an additional dimension. Wrapped up in every object somehow there is a fourth measure: time.

Just think: If you made an appointment to meet someone, it would not be enough to say, "On the fifth floor of the building on the corner of Main and Second." You would have to specify the time.

Again, if you were teaching someone a tune on the piano you would have to show your pupil *where* on the piano the notes were and how *long* to hold them. In the night sky there is an illustration of how time is one

of the four measures of things. Fix your gaze upon a
star. Do you see it?

You are mistaken. The star is not where you see it.
Stars are so far away that it takes years, in some cases
many thousands of years, for their light to reach us.
Meanwhile the stars themselves have moved on. What
you are looking at, therefore, is not the star itself, but
its leftover image. Time, you see, is tied into space.

We live in a world where events have four dimensions, a world not of space *and* time, but of space-time.
Moreover, it is a world in which physical laws can be
understood only by comparing or relating events to
each other. The single exception, the one event that is
not relative but absolute and constant, is the speed of
light.

IV

Among scientists the atmosphere began to crackle
with questions. How does the pull of gravity fit into
this new theory? How does the force of acceleration
with which bodies fall in space fit into it? These were
the two most formidable questions.

Einstein reasoned in this fashion: Imagine that you
are in an elevator at the top floor of a very tall building.
Suppose that the elevator begins to fall freely, faster
and ever faster. You drop a handkerchief. Instead of
falling to the floor, it remains floating in space. Objects
and people are as weightless in such an elevator as if it
were gliding in outer space, free from the earth's pull.
On the other hand, if you were in a spaceship suddenly
accelerated by a booster rocket, its floor would suddenly

press upward on your feet, and your earth weight would be restored. Objects would fall just as you have always experienced. As the spaceship continued to accelerate, the effect inside the ship would be the same as the familiar pull of the earth. These two fields of force, gravity and acceleration, at any point of space are in every way equivalent, Einstein concluded. No experiment could possibly distinguish between them.

Albert Einstein sought for ways to test his theories. An opportunity came in 1919 when an eclipse of the sun was about to occur. In advance of the eclipse he predicted that stars located near the sun would appear to shift. "Pick a star from your charts," he suggested to astronomers. "At the instant when the moon's disc covers the sun totally and the stars are brilliant in a black sky. Then photograph the area close to the sun. Compare the photograph with your star chart. You will find that the stars in the sky near the eclipsed sun will seem to have shifted their positions just a bit. The path of the light rays will be slightly bent by the pull of the sun. My calculations should be checked."

British astronomers traveled to the coasts of West Africa and also Brazil where the eclipse was to be total. The learned world waited excitedly for the outcome of this, the first test of the Einstein general theory of relativity. The result was precisely as he had predicted.

What did it mean?

It meant, explained Einstein, that when starlight passes the sun, the starlight bends as though around a curve. To us it appears as though the star itself has shifted . . . Another way of explaining the phenomenon is that light takes the shortest path. If the path is curved near massive bodies like the sun, then space itself must be curved there. We may be living in a world where Euclid's geometry does not hold throughout.

People educated in the ancient mathematics were indignant. "It cannot be! It cannot be that we live in so queer a world!"

That sounded familiar. It was, in fact, exactly what people said when they first heard that the earth moves round the sun.

Einstein's theory has withstood every test. In order to fit his relativity ideas into our science, Isaac Newton's theory had to be modified. Scientists were thus forced to change all their views of the universe, as they had to do in the time of Copernicus.

V

Even if Einstein had never discovered the laws of relativity, he would still be a hero of science, for he clarified another long-standing mystery.

Tiny grains of pollen dancing about, and defying the law of gravity! That sight amazed a Scottish botanist, Dr. Robert Brown, as he peered through his microscope at pollen grains zigzagging through the liquid.

"I understand why they do not sink — that's because they are too light. Then, since they are light, why don't they float? What makes them dance about? Are they alive?"

He divided various solids finely — so finely that he could just see the tiny particles in the liquid through his microscope. Still they danced. No matter what kinds

of particles he used or what fluid he floated them on,
the particles darted back and forth.

For nearly a hundred years, scientists were puzzled
by this Brownian movement of particles too small to be
seen except through powerful microscopes. They
offered various explanations.

"Perhaps it is because one part of the liquid is colder
than the other."

"Perhaps it is the way light shines on them that
makes them dance about."

"Perhaps they are tiny tremblings caused by heavy
wagons passing along the street."

All such explanations of Brownian movement were
erroneous and scientists discarded every one. They
agreed on one thing, that the dancing movement was
being performed by molecules.

What are molecules? On this too scientists agreed.
Their explanation was somewhat as follows: Consider
a very small sample of any substance whether solid, gas
or liquid. Let's try water. Take a drop of it. Divide the
drop in half. Now divide this in half. Continue dividing
until the droplet is too small to be seen by the eye alone.
Imagine it divided so finely that it cannot be seen with
the help of the most powerful microscope. At this point
you approach the final stage of the droplet of water. If
you attempt to divide it further it will cease to be water
and will break down into two gases: hydrogen and
oxygen. That final stage is the water molecule.

The question arose: If you cannot see a molecule,
how do you know what it is? And the answer: by the
way it behaves. Molecules are like the tiniest rubber
balls bouncing back and forth. When hundreds of

molecules of water bombard grains of pollen they cause them to zigzag and dance about.

That much scientists knew about Brownian movement. But it wasn't enough. Science is never satisfied with an explanation until it is put in the form of a mathematical law that can be tested.

That law was discovered by the twenty-six-year-old Albert Einstein.

VI

Honors came to this "Newton of the twentieth century" from all sides: the Nobel Prize in 1921, honorary degrees from universities, invitations to lecture. When he visited the United States, his lecture halls could not hold all the people who sought admission. And yet there was no one more modest or unassuming. He did not seem to be conscious of being the most eminent scientist alive and one of the greatest of all time. Delegations of civic leaders would go to meet the world-renowned Albert Einstein at a railroad station and they saw a bareheaded man with unruly hair and a shy smile, carelessly dressed, a violin case under his arm.

In 1933 he was invited to become a professor at the Institute of Advanced Studies at Princeton. There, for the rest of his life, he was occupied with the most sublime of all problems in science.

"Can I find a principle," he asked himself, "a simple scientific law to explain natural phenomena from electrons to nebulae? Can I construct a mathematical model of our universe from atom to Milky Way?

This was the dream Albert Einstein dared to dream.

To the end of his days he kept before him the vision of a unified theory, as he called it, and he died believing it could be found. It remains as his challenge and his legacy to the present generation of scientists.

BOOK III
Heroes
of Invention

Johann Gutenberg

(c. 1400–c. 1468)

THOUGHTS NEVER DIE

I

"Do you realize that if this rumor is true," an English scientist explained to his Chinese secretary, "the history of Asia will have to be revised? Who knows what treasures may lie among those ruins?"

"You shall see," the secretary calmly replied.

They were crossing the plains and deserts of northwestern China in the spring of 1907, bound for the city of Tunhwang. They cared little about the dilapidated Chinese town, but nearby were the ruins of what once was a famous Buddhist monastery, the Caves of the Thousand Buddhas.

The sand-covered hills and the desert valleys only added to Sir Aurel Stein's zeal for his enterprise. He felt he must see the library of thousands of manuscripts that had so strangely been discovered here. What might these new documents not tell about the history of China, of India, of Turkestan?

They entered a desert valley. On all sides rose sheer cliffs. One cliff, Sir Aurel Stein noticed, was honeycombed with dark holes. "There seem to be countless grottoes in that rock," he remarked.

Huge sand dunes covered a great part of the cliff, and the grottoes looked as though they had been crumbling away through centuries. But two of them were somehow marked, and the travelers stepped into their gloomy interiors. In the half-light they made out that they were in the midst of venerable shrines, with gigantic statues of Buddha, ninety feet high!

A young Chinese approached them. It was Ho-shang, who helped care for the ancient shrine.

"There is a rumor," the Englishman explained, "that many manuscripts have been found here. I have come far to look at these books of wisdom."

"My master, Wang Tao-shih, has locked them in a secret chamber. He himself is not here now. I expect him in about three weeks."

"Must I then wait three long weeks before I can see the manuscripts?"

"If you wish to see the paintings and statues," Ho-shang suggested, "I shall be very glad to show you. Many are over a thousand years old."

The plastered walls were alive with most interesting pictures. "They all tell the story of Buddha," said Ho-shang.

But Sir Aurel Stein was more concerned about another matter. "How did your master discover the books?" he asked.

"About seven years ago my master raised some money to restore the ruins of our grottoes, which he loves, to their former glory. While cleaning one of the paintings, the laborers discovered a crack in the wall, which showed it to be brick and not rock. When my master broke through the brick wall, he found himself in a chamber cut in the rock and filled with thousands of manuscripts and beautiful banners of silk."

"I wonder why the room had been walled up."

"Ah! About nine hundred years ago," Ho-shang explained, "the monks sealed the chamber so that the valuable things here might not fall into the hands of enemies."

"I see. Thank you."

The genial Ho-shang could do no more for the Englishman. Sir Aurel Stein had to be content to wait the three weeks for the arrival of Wang Tao-shih. And he would be more than content if the Chinese master would admit him to the locked chamber of manuscripts.

The day came when the English archaeologist was at last in the presence of Wang Tao-shih.

The Chinese scholar heard his plea. "Is it the wisdom of Buddha the English student is eager for?"

Sir Aurel Stein nodded vigorously.

It was enough. Wang Tao-shih led the way through grottoes colored with paintings and gilded statues. Then they came to the secret chamber. Sir Aurel Stein's eyes sparkled as the dim light of Wang Tao-shih's lamp flickered across a room packed to its ceiling with bundles of manuscripts and banners.

"What happiness will be mine if you permit me to examine some of these treasures!" pleaded the excited archaeologist.

Roll after roll Wang Tao-shih handed to Chiang, who read the title aloud. The Englishman was beside himself with joy. "A Sanskrit volume!" he exclaimed. "A Turkish prayer book! And a . . ." The floor was littered with fragments of books in every Eastern language.

"Look at these banners!" Wang pointed to a painted banner of transparent silk gauze.

"What harmony of color! And such skill in drawing!" admired the Englishman. He did not know whether to marvel more at these silken banners, whose golds and reds and greens were as fresh as if they had been painted that morning, or at the paper that had been made at least a thousand years ago — long before Europe had even heard of paper.

As Chiang was glancing through the bundles of writing, he was attracted by an interesting-looking roll. It contained one picture. "Look! This book is printed!" he exclaimed.

"What is it? Read it!" demanded the Englishman.

" 'Thus have I heard,' intoned Chiang, 'concerning the Master Buddha. Upon a memorable occasion, Buddha sojourned in the Kingdom of Shravasti, and lodged in the grove of Jeta.' " The walls of the old grotto rang.

" '. . . With the Master Buddha were twelve hundred fifty disciples, all of whom had attained great learning . . . The noble Subhiti, his chief disciple, was in the midst of the assembly. He arose from his seat, and kneeling upon his right knee, he pressed together the palms of his hands and raised them towards Buddha. He exclaimed: "Thou, who hast such great understanding, O most Honored One, what must your disciples do to obtain perfect wisdom?" ' "

"It is *The Diamond Sutra!*" said the Englishman solemnly.

"Yes," replied Wang Tao-shih, "and rightly named. Just as the diamond excels all other precious gems in brilliance, so the wisdom of this book surpasses that of other books."

"Let me look at it closely."

As he touched the aged Chinese book, Sir Aurel Stein agreed with Chiang that it was printed, printed by carved wooden blocks.

"Do you know what that means?" he cried. "This is the oldest printed book in the world!"

For *The Diamond Sutra,* now in the British Museum, had been printed in 868 — six hundred years before the invention of printing in Europe.

It was indeed unfortunate that Europe had not known of the splendid old civilization of China. Since they had not, it meant that brave men of Europe had to blaze new paths to the same goal. Printing had to be invented all over again . . .

II

In 1420 Johann Gutenberg wandered gloomily from his home, the German city of Mainz. The youth was — or rather had been — well-to-do, but was now a political exile forbidden to enter the gates of his native city. He was on his way to Strasbourg, which, he was told, was a city that had respect for books and learning.

Johann was not too worried about earning a living. He had learned the skills of a goldsmith, an art in great demand in those days.

One grand thought erased some of the harshness of exile. Johann felt that in Strasbourg he would achieve his goal — to perfect a printing press so that he could publish thousands of copies of a book.

It had all started when his father showed him a deck of playing cards. Johann remembered saying, "An artist must have spent much time drawing the pictures on the cards."

His father explained: "No. These pictures are not hand-drawn. The one who made this deck of cards used wood blocks. He carved a drawing for each card on a block of wood. For instance, on one block he drew the king of spades, and on another the queen of spades. He then cut away the block around the design, leaving a raised and therefore ink-catching letter. The artist brushed ink over the surface of the wood block. Every time he pressed a paper on the inked block, an image of the artist's drawing was produced. He used the wood block over and over again, and stamped the same picture on many cards. In this way he made perhaps a dozen decks of playing cards."

"Are those decks of cards alike?"

"Some day I shall show you another deck. You will convince yourself that no artist could draw two copies of the same picture as alike as they are on the playing cards."

When Johann did see two decks of cards together, he was amazed at their likeness. From then on he practiced carving wood blocks. He soon discovered that for the picture to be printed correctly, the wood blocks had to be carved with the design in reverse. If one could carve a picture and reproduce it many times, he wondered, could one do the same with a page of a book? As the exile neared Strasbourg, he reviewed in his mind the attempts he had made to print a page. The blocks fitted together badly. He could not make the rows of print form straight lines. The ink impressions were not uniform. The results of experimenting with wood blocks were discouraging.

Yet he must work on. The world needed books, many books. How could people rise above ignorance unless they could read? Books should be cheap so that everyone could afford to buy them.

At that time in the entire Mainz region one found perhaps no more than a few hundred volumes in all the monasteries and churches, and an additional hundred possessed by the nobles and the rich.

Johann Gutenberg knew that books could not reach all the people as long as they had to rely on scribes, who sat with their quill pens at their sloping desks and industriously copied other handwritten volumes. He must continue with the printing press in spite of all obstacles.

III

As he stepped into the city of Strasbourg, he saw that unlike Mainz the streets were paved with smooth stones. There were, however, familiar sights: narrow streets with houses whose second stories overhung the shops on the ground floor; streets crowded with horsemen, merchants, and workmen; dogs barking and children playing.

Johann Gutenberg brought with him from Mainz enough money so that he could begin without delay his experiments on printing. His thoughts constantly recurred to the printed page. A book page is not one unit like a playing card, but is made up of many units, the letters of the alphabet. Therefore, his type must have much greater precision than he had achieved with a block of wood. Why not fashion metal type for each letter?

He began to cut individual letters on pieces of metal. Hours of painstaking labor were required to engrave and polish each of these bits of type. His purpose was to make all the letters that he would need for the words that make up a page.

One day Gutenberg reflected on his hard, slow work. "At this rate I shall have to fashion almost a thousand letters just to print one page! What if I wanted to print a book as large as the Bible?" he asked himself. "Then I would have to set every person in Strasbourg to work for me to make the type! This is ridiculous." It had become clear to him that he must devise a better method of making type.

It occurred to Gutenberg that in producing his type he could perhaps use the process that he had observed in the Mainz mint when hundreds of coins were stamped out, each with an identical design. At the mint he remembered watching an artist make a design for a coin in wax. The design was cut into a bar of soft steel by an engraver. The lettering was then hammered into the bar. To harden the steel, the "punch," or die, was heated. In the same way, the punch for the other side of the coin was made.

A gold disc, much softer than the hardened steel, would then be placed between the two punches. As heavy hammers pounded the two punches together, the design engraved on the punches was pressed onto the softer gold. In this way new coins were minted.

Just as the mint made punches for coins, Gutenberg decided to make punches — one for each letter of the alphabet. "What I intend to do is more delicate than the work in the mint," he thought. "Pounding with heavy hammers would shatter my fragile type."

He had watched a goldsmith make an ornament. To make a replica of a gold brooch, he filled the two halves of a box with damp sand. He laid the brooch on the sand in one half of the box and closed the box. When he opened it and took the brooch out, the shape of the brooch was clearly impressed into the damp sand. Now the goldsmith made a hole in the cover of the box and poured melted gold or silver into the sand impression, so that when the metal cooled, it was in the shape of the brooch.

Gutenberg did the same with the letters of the alphabet. He made a punch for each letter in brass. He then cast in an amalgam of tin and lead as many copies of the letter as he wanted.

In time he learned how to cast type in large quantities, and how to make the mold for each letter with great precision. He also developed a special ink to be used for printing on paper.

The printing press that Gutenberg built was finally ready. The first book he printed was a Latin grammer.

The grammar which he had studied as a youth had been copied out on parchment by the hand of a professional scribe. Gutenberg decided to print a hundred copies of the book.

The Latin grammar was a trial run of the press, and Gutenberg was happy with the results. After he had set the type for a page, the actual printing of it took so little time that he could print a dozen copies of the page in the time it took a scribe to make one copy only. The twenty-eight-page book astounded the learned. It was hard for them to believe that its pages were not written by a scribe.

Johann Gutenberg was now ready for a formidable task. He undertook to print the book that was most frequently used in Europe: the Bible. It was slow, painstaking work. The publication of the Bible, however, caused great excitement. Here was a book printed on paper that was as attractive as a book handwritten on vellum, and much cheaper.

Within one generation the printing press displaced the scribe. First came a trickle, which has since increased into a steady flow, of books, magazines and newspapers to communicate comfort and pleasure and information.

With his printing press, Johann Gutenberg ushered in a new era of civilization.

Robert Fulton

(1765–1815)

FOR THE SAKE OF HUMANITY

I

A GAY CITY is afloat on the Atlantic. The walks, lined
with easy chairs, under the twinkling lights, are fresh
with the summer scent of the sea. Now and then a
stroller steps into view, only to disappear in a bend of
the long walk. From the doors leading into a lounge
and ballroom come the murmur of conversation and
the strains of music. The library is bright, but deserted,
for most of its patrons have gone to the theater. Its
thousands of people are enjoying life to the fullest. In
the morning, the sport of the gymnasium, the swimming pool, and the vigorous games in the open will
displace the nightly brilliance of the ballroom.

The gay city is a modern ocean liner. It is one-fifth of
a mile in length and four stories high. It weighs fifty
thousand tons and speeds along at more than twenty-
five miles an hour. Surrounded by every luxury, its passengers gaze fearlessly over the rail into the water.

Not always did the sea offer to travelers as little risk
as now. Once, in unknown days, a man must have sat on
the shore of a wide river brooding on the mystery be-

fore him — the nourishing deep, the deadly deep.
Across the watery chasm a lovely shore beckoned the
hero with its plentiful game and far green hills. How
much more delightful to be there than here! But wish
as he would, the way was blocked. The water between
him and the shore was deep and treacherous. The current was stronger than muscle.

"If I could only have a willing fish that would float
me to the new shore!" he wished.

All at once he was startled by a sight he had seen
often but never so vividly. It was the branch of a tree
floating easily down the river. It gave him an idea.

"I shall have a wooden fish," was the thought that
came with a leap. He tried out his great idea. A log in
the water bore him, lying flat on it. Then, the branch of
a tree in hand, he paddled his way about. Although he
did not yet dare strike out for that green shore, he was
delighted with his new means of traveling. It was a
grand adventure.

And it led to something much grander. The log
cramped him for room. So why not tie a few logs together? It was not long before a raft was built, and our
hero was ferrying not only himself but also his bows
and arrows, his friends, his animals, and provisions.

Once an especially wide log gave someone else a new
idea. "If it were hollow, so that I could sit in it and not
on it, I should have a speedy bark instead of a clumsy
raft," he said. Soon he was gliding along in his first
canoe.

Crude it may have been, but once caught by the ex-
hilaration of speed, another quickly improved his dug-
out. "This sturdy wood," he believed, "can stand being

hollowed until it is just a shell so it will be lighter, speedier, and easier to steer."

He found he was right. With a little skill in wielding his broad paddle, he was at home on either shore of the river.

One lucky day, as he was journeying far down the stream, he felt his canoe fairly leap over the water. The shore rushed past him with unusual speed. The breeze was wafting him along. He scarcely needed his paddle. "Why not catch more of the breeze," he thought boldly, "and let it do all the work for me?" He hoisted a skin square against the wind, and sailed merrily on. No longer did he have to push himself through the water. He only steered.

His new craft was all elegance and grace. Breezing along in it, he and his companions felt as safe as fishes. With trust in their hearts and a wind in their sail, they no longer needed to stay in the mild inland waters.

"I must go down to the sea," he sang. And dancing on the waves, with the spray on his cheek, he came to know the wild wonder of the sea.

At first, of course, even the most daring sailors feared to venture too far from land. Prudently, they hugged the coast with its familiar landmarks. They sailed by day, but at night they beached their boats and slept on the shore. In time, men learned to steer by the sun during the daytime and by the stars at night. Then they could sail fearlessly in the open sea, land out of sight.

The ship sailed faster and faster. Longer grew the craft. Galleys a hundred feet long, with the prow of a swan's neck and pulled by three rows of oarsmen, carried strange cargoes of merchandise across foreign wa-

ters. The sailors' yarns were even stranger. The timid
landlubbers felt the romance of the sea.

Yet the wind sometimes died or rose high with disaster. Stately Spanish galleons and English carracks were
playthings to the breeze. As the Ancient Mariner said:

> *Down dropt the breeze, the sails dropt down,*
> *'Twas sad as sad could be;*
> *And we did speak only to break*
> *The silence of the sea!*
>
> .   .   .   .   .
>
> *Day after day, day after day,*
> *We stuck, nor breath nor motion;*
> *As idle as a painted ship*
> *Upon a painted ocean.*

Must men be slaves to the wind always? "Perhaps
with the aid of the new power, steam, our sailors might
become more free." So hoped a few dreamers — John
Fitch in America, and William Symington in England.
But man's understanding of the power of steam was yet
too slight.

II

Two men were deep in talk. One was especially
lively. His tall, graceful person was bent tensely forward, and his large, dark eyes fixed expressively on his
friend.

"It is now 1807," he was saying energetically. "Allow
me to play prophet. By 1850, there will not be a single
sailing vessel among our water craft, except for idle
pleasure."

The other smiled. "Fulton," he said, "you are indeed

persuasive, but my better judgment tells me you are a false prophet. How can a bit of an engine, of the kind you describe, propel a ship the size of your *Clermont?*"

"It is Watt's engine," Robert Fulton replied. "That is sufficient recommendation. It will in time do much more than propel ships. Well!" He rose to go. "Then you will not lend me the thousand dollars I need to finish the *Clermont?*"

His friend shook his head. Then as Fulton turned dejectedly, he called, "Wait! Suppose I gave you one hundred dollars. It would help, wouldn't it — provided you could raise nine hundred more?"

Fulton thanked him.

"I make one condition," his friend went on. "You must keep this a secret. I am sure that your other lenders will also wish their names withheld. You see," he explained with some embarrassment, "the public, on whom I depend for business, thinks you mad. They call the *Clermont* 'Fulton's Folly.' "

"I know," said Fulton with a sigh, "even my friends . . . And as I pass to and from the shipyard, I often loiter unknown near idle groups, from whom I hear nothing but scorn and sneers. Someone says 'Fulton's Folly.' At once everybody rocks with laughter. We shall see, though."

He left. The next few days he spent raising the nine hundred dollars, and whoever lent him money made the same condition: his name was to be kept secret. No one wished to be involved with "Fulton's Folly" — as though it were folly to work for human progress.

While Fulton had been in France the United States had purchased Louisiana — that vast land watered by

the Mississippi. For commerce, this river was a one-way
stream. A loaded barge could be floated down to New
Orleans and the sea, but the strong current prevented
bringing a cargo back.

Fulton thought of this. He decided to make it possible for a ship to overcome the strong current of the
Mississippi with the steam engine. "In this way," said
he, "the settlers will be able to get their supplies without that long and difficult crossing of the mountains."
He bought an engine from Watt's factory and returned
with it to the United States. With the engine turning
the paddles of a boat, he intended to solve the problem
of commerce.

On a day in August, 1807, at a dock in the North
River, New York City, the *Clermont* stood ready for its
trial voyage up the Hudson. It was a queer-looking
craft. The machinery, in the center, was open to view.
Thick, black smoke belched from the smokestack.
Steam hissed from every valve of the engine. The paddle wheels, unprotected, swung heavily at each side and
splashed the water as they turned.

People filled the wharves, the housetops, and every
spot from which they could look on. Fulton's friends
were gathered in groups on the dock. There was anxiety mixed with fear among them. They were silent, sad,
and weary. Fulton read in their looks nothing but disaster. At one o'clock the signal was given, and the *Clermont* was loosed from its moorings. As it moved on a
short distance, the onlookers were tense and silent.
Suddenly, a creaking of machinery, and the boat
stopped.

"I told you so!"

"What could you expect!"

"A stupid scheme!"

"Poor Fulton! He would not take advice."

"Fulton's Folly!"

Many more contemptuous remarks condemned the inventor. But the clear, sharp voice of Fulton was heard above the hum of the multitude and the noise of the engine. He had climbed up on a platform and began to address the crowd. He did not know what was the matter, he stated, but if they would be quiet and patient for half an hour, he would either go on or abandon the voyage for that time.

"A fair request," murmured the people.

Fulton went below and examined the machinery. The trouble was slight, he discovered, and in a short time it was righted. The boat was again put in motion. She continued to move on. The crowd was still incredulous. Not a soul was willing to believe his eyes.

But as the boat continued, a cry arose and grew louder, until finally everyone was cheering as lustily as he could and praising Fulton as warmly as before he had condemned him. The hero of their cheers stood erect upon the deck, his dark eyes flashing.

The *Clermont* glided by New York. It passed through the romantic and ever-varying scenery of the Highlands. From many points of the river, whence the boat could be seen, inhabitants collected. They waved their handkerchiefs and hurrahed for Fulton.

On kept the *Clermont,* on, until the clustering houses of Albany were seen. The one hundred and fifty miles between New York and Albany had been covered in only thirty-two hours, while the sailboats took forty-eight hours when the wind was good.

The day was glorious for Robert Fulton. The steamboat was now a fact.

> *But why drives on that ship so fast,*
> *Without or wave or wind?*

When Samuel Taylor Coleridge wrote those lines, he thought of a ghost ship. But in his wildest ghostly imaginings, he could never have dreamed that his American friend Robert Fulton would build such a ship.

In a short while, the *Clermont* was making regular trips up the Hudson, well filled with passengers. The rules posted on the cabin walls prove how trim and well kept she was. One rule read, "It is not permitted for any person to lie down in a berth with their boots or shoes on, under penalty of $1.50 and 50 cents for every half hour they may offend against this rule."

III

A few years before Fulton built the *Clermont,* he made another invention in Paris, a submarine. It was his pet among all his inventions — and he had many to his credit.

At the age of ten he had said to his schoolmaster, who had reproved him for not studying his books, "My head is so full of my own ideas that there is no room for the storage of dusty books." Even at that early age, he had showed his mechanical bent. But he could draw and paint pictures so skillfully that he chose the career of an artist. So well did he do at portraits and landscapes in his studio in Philadelphia that at the age of twenty-one he could afford to buy his widowed mother a farm. But he had worked so hard that his health had suffered, and he was forced to take a sea trip to recover.

He sailed for England. Here, too, he was busy as a portrait painter. But innumerable ideas of inventions began to occupy his time and crowded out art. Reluctantly, he put paintbrush and canvas aside, turning to them only for recreation. While he was in Europe, the French Revolution broke out. The king was deposed, and France dared the world to set him back again on the throne. For the next twenty years there was constant war, especially between England and France. Fulton was vividly reminded of the horrors of his childhood, when he had been in the very midst of the American Revolution.

As a man who had witnessed the miseries of war until his soul was sick, he thought, "How can war be ended? How can the nations become as close as a family of brothers?" He thought that perhaps if they could communicate more readily with each other, hostility would cease. But how could they communicate more readily? Why not a system of canals? Canals would be of great benefit to all. Goods could be transported more cheaply by boat than by wagon. In that way, thought Fulton, living would become cheaper and easier.

He improved locks and other machinery to make canals more efficient. He invented a device to carry boats overland from one canal to another.

"I look forward to a time when canals will pass through every vale," he said, "and . . . around every

hill, binding whole countries together in social bonds."
He was the first to think of a canal across the state of
New York — the Erie Canal.

It seems, moreover, that while he was in the inventing mood, he designed a machine to saw marble, one to
spin flax, and one to make rope. He designed a digging
machine for constructing canals, an aqueduct, and a
device for clearing stumps of trees from the line of the
intended canal. How simple to mention these many
machines in a few words! Perhaps for so brilliant a man
as Fulton these tasks were not difficult, but they took
years of his manhood.

How could war be prevented? He thought about this
constantly. What made war possible? England, for instance, was able to bring the United States into war in
1775 by means of her navy . . . Solved! A simple machine which would sink navies as easily as a pin bursts a
bubble.

As his mind became stimulated with the idea, he
considered more and more clearly the engine he
needed. "There is a fish," he recalled, "a torpedo fish,
which paralyzes and kills its victims by an electric
shock."

A mechanical torpedo fish! A boat that could ply
under water, a submarine, armed with the weapon of
the torpedo!

He began to study the physiology of the fish; how it
was able to lower and raise itself in the water. The result of this study was the first diving boat, the *Nautilus*.
Fulton tested his submarine on the Seine River, near
Paris. He and a sailor shut themselves in, with a single
candle, and remained under water for three hours. Im-

agine the outburst from the crowd of French people lining the banks when the *Nautilus,* like a long, narrow egg, slowly emerged from the water.

For a torpedo, Fulton used a copper bowl filled with gunpowder. It had a trigger which caused it to explode as soon as it struck its target. The destroying power of the submarine and its torpedo was first tested by the French navy. A small sloop was anchored. Fulton advanced the *Nautilus* to within two hundred feet of her and fired his bomb. The explosion which followed was so great that a column of water, smoke, and splinters shot up for one hundred feet in the air.

Fulton now returned to America and offered to the United States his terrible engine of war to destroy war. "In the hands of a righteous nation," said he, "my submarine will insure universal peace."

Far from being grateful to him, not a soul believed in the usefulness of this invention. "It can't possibly work," people declared. "No bomb can explode under water by clockwork."

Fulton laughed. "Let me put one of my bombs under water," he suggested. "If you don't believe it can explode by clockwork, sail over it!"

No one wanted to commit suicide, and Fulton was able to justify his claims.

Aside from his having perfected the steamboat and invented the submarine, Fulton's greatest hold on us is his desire for eternal peace in the human family.

Samuel Finley Breese Morse

(1791–1872)

ELECTRICITY, THE MESSENGER

I

On an autumn day about a hundred and thirty years ago, the *Sully* was steaming in mid-ocean towards New York from the shore of France. In its dining room a party of passengers were enjoying an after-dinner chat. Among the number were Dr. Charles T. Jackson of Boston and the well-known artist Samuel Morse of New York. Dr. Jackson had brought up the subject of electricity, still a young science at that time.

"A wonderful object," he was saying, "is this electromagnet that the Englishman Sturgeon has invented. It is so simple! Just a piece of iron, curved like a horseshoe."

"Why, how does it work, Doctor?" Morse asked.

"Some copper wire is twined around the iron. Whenever an electric current passes through the wire, the iron becomes a magnet."

"By the way, Doctor," asked someone else, "what is the speed of electricity through a wire?"

"Instantaneous," replied Jackson. "Franklin found

that out in Philadelphia. He stretched a wire across the Schuylkill River. When he touched the wire on one bank with electricity, at the same moment a spark shot out from the wire on the opposite bank."

There was a silence for a while; everyone's thoughts were busy. Suddenly the artist Morse struck the table lightly with his fist. He leaned forward.

"Doctor," he began in measured tones, "have you ever been on the Italian frontier?"

"Yes. Well?"

"And have you seen the semaphore signals they send there?"

"Oh, yes," said Dr. Jackson. "They can send messages that way for several miles. What of it?"

Morse did not answer directly. Then his words came slowly: "If the presence of electricity can be made visible in any part of the circuit, why can't we signal messages that way? We could send news one thousand miles in a flash, we could . . ."

He looked eloquently about him. Everyone was smiling incredulously. Morse felt that he impressed them as a daydreamer.

He retired to his cabin. For the rest of the voyage he brooded in solitude, either in his cabin or on deck, but he drew much in his sketchbook. He was determined to work out the idea of using electricity to carry messages. He was not a novice in experimenting with electricity or electromagnetism. He had often assisted his neighbor, Professor Benjamin Silliman of Yale University, in laboratory experiments on batteries and electrical currents.

When the ship finally docked at New York, Morse

went down the gangplank, and stopped before the captain of the vessel. "Well, Captain," said he, "should you hear of the 'telegraph' one of these days as the wonder of the world, remember the discovery was made on the good ship *Sully*."

II

On his return to New York, Morse wanted to begin his work on the telegraph. His plan was to use for his experiments the money he made as a painter of pictures. But to his alarm he found that he could not even make enough money for his own bare needs. He had been away for three years improving his art in Europe. And now other artists had become popular. Nobody came to ask him to paint a portrait. He found himself in the strong clutch of poverty. Although he lived in one room and ate little but tea and crackers, his landlord and grocer pressed him more than any scientific experiments.

He became a private teacher of art, but his pupils were few. No one knew how much Morse really suffered, and only occasionally could it be suspected. Once, when he went to give a lesson to a pupil who owed him money, he asked courteously, "Well, my boy, how are we off for money?"

"Why, Professor," the student answered, "I expect to have some money next week."

"Next week," Morse repeated sadly. "I shall be dead by that time."

"Dead, sir?"

"Yes, dead by starvation."

The student appeared distressed and astonished. Then he said hurriedly, "Would ten dollars be of any service?"

"Ten dollars," exclaimed Morse good-humoredly, "would save my life! That is all it would do."

Gaily the two hastened to a restaurant. After a modest meal, Morse said jokingly, "This is my first meal for twenty-four hours. My boy, don't be an artist. It means beggary."

Just the same, Morse found time to conduct his experiments. As for money, he did not need much. He had an inventive mind and could do with the simplest materials: an old picture frame, the wheels of an old wooden clock, three wooden drums, a few wires, a few boards, a piece of iron — very little, in fact, that he could not pick up in the street as rubbish. Up in that dreary room of his — bedroom, studio, workroom, living room, all in one — he toiled with such materials for months.

Countless difficulties had to be resolved. For instance, how could a message be sent by means of a wire? Could his apparatus transmit signals that would be recognized by the person receiving the message? And could he make these signals into a code that would be understood easily?

Morse experimented with various combinations of dots and dashes to construct such a code. Finally, he set up twenty-six combinations of dots and dashes to stand for the letters in the alphabet. We call it the Morse Code.

At last his model was built, and he was off to Washington with it. To a committee of Congressmen he showed how it worked. It was wonderful, they agreed. And so simple! Touch a key at one end of a wire, an electric current flashed through the wire, the *rat-tat-tat* delivered a message at the other end. How? By a code: a short and a long flash — A, two longs — M, and so on.

"Wonderful!" said the Congressmen.

Morse said he was proud to be the one through whom distant people could be drawn closer together. He was proud to serve humanity with his invention, but he would need $30,000 to put it to the test. Would Congress give it?

Every man in the committee thought Congress would. Morse waited. He could do nothing else. His fate and the fate of the telegraph were in the hands of a busy Congress. For years poor Morse waited, living from hand to mouth, until, completely discouraged, he wrote bitterly to a friend: "I find myself without sympathy or help from anyone. For nearly two years past, I have given all my time and scanty means, denying myself all pleasure and even necessary food. I am crushed. Unless I have the means from some source, I shall be compelled to give up the matter. Nothing but the knowledge that I have an invention which is to contribute to the happiness of millions has sustained me."

Then, in March, 1843, just as his fortunes were at the lowest ebb, when he had less than one dollar in the whole world, Congress passed the bill to appropriate $30,000 for an experimental telegraph line! It was passed during the last hour of the session by a vote of 89 to 83.

Morse was the happiest man alive. He began the

work of stringing his wires between Washington and
Baltimore. The world knew little of his invention.
Those who did know were doubtful of its importance.
When the wiring was finished, Morse thought, and the
first message sent, the world could judge.

One day he was setting up his telegraph in a room of
the Capitol. To locate his wires, he had to go down to a
vault which had long been closed. In the cellar he
found the vault, dim and dusty. It took some time for
his eyes to become accustomed to the gloom. Presently
he was able to see fairly well, when he was attracted by
something white, shining in the darkness. It seemed a
familiar object. He approached it quickly. It was a
statue that he had sculptured in his very young days. He
had given it to an architect of the Capitol, who had laid
it aside and forgotten all about it.

"Ah!" It started a train of memory, recalling his artistic career. He remembered how, when he was but
four at Old Ma'am Rand's school, he had been whipped
many a time for drawing funny pictures of her. And
when his father sent him at sixteen to Yale, he paid his
way by drawing "miniatures on ivory for $5 each, or
profiles for $1."

What a passion he had had for art! "No human
power can destroy it," he had confidently said. He certainly never dreamed of becoming an inventor; no, not
though as a boy he had once invented a pump and later
a sculpturing machine.

He had gone to England to study art, and there had
met the great American painter Benjamin West. He
remembered showing a drawing of his to the great artist. What a lesson he had had then!

"Very well, sir, very well; go on and finish it," West had said.

"But it is finished."

"Oh, no," said West, "see here, and here. And here are places you can improve."

He had gone back to his drawing. After a week he had felt confident and again showed it to West.

Again West had said approvingly, "Very well indeed, sir; go on and finish it."

"Is it not finished?" Morse remembered the sinking of his heart.

"Not yet. See, you have not marked that muscle and those finger joints."

For three days more he had struggled with the drawing. And all that West had finally said was, "Very clever indeed, but go on and finish it."

"I cannot finish it," was the despairing reply.

"Well," the master had confessed, "I have tried you long enough. Now, sir, you have learned more by this drawing than you would have by doing a dozen others. It is not numerous drawings that make an artist, but a single perfect one."

This lesson he had never forgotten. It had helped him to become a good artist, so good that the City of New York had selected him from many to paint the portrait of that benefactor of the United States, Lafayette; so good that he had been elected for almost twenty years in succession the president of the National Academy of Design. Who knows what fame had awaited him as an artist? But he had become interested in the study of electricity. The persistence Benjamin West had

taught him in drawing, he had given to the telegraph.
And now he was on the eve of a great test . . .

III

May 24, 1844.

The last wire had been strung. Morse stood before
his instrument in Washington. In Baltimore — forty
miles away — before another instrument stood his
friend Alfred Vail. An audience of people surrounded
both. Morse was plainly excited. The great test had
come. He had to send some message.

"What shall I say?"

"Say this," suggested a young woman. " 'What hath
God wrought!' "

With nervous fingers Morse began to click a patter
on the key . . .

In Baltimore, the silent instrument that many were
watching suddenly began to flash a *rat-tat-tat.* It was
magical. Then just as suddenly it stopped.

"What did it say?" asked the crowd breathlessly.

Vail deciphered the message. "It said, 'What hath
God wrought!' "

The public was too amazed to believe their senses.
Not until two days later, when the Democratic national convention met at Baltimore, was it convinced.
The convention nominated James K. Polk for President and Silas Wright for Vice-President. Mr. Wright
was in Washington at the time.

Alfred Vail telegraphed the news to Morse in Washington, who at once told Mr. Wright. Wright declined

the nomination. A few minutes later, Vail presented the news to the convention at Baltimore.

The members of the convention were dumb-founded. They would not believe it. A committee was at once sent to Washington to see Mr. Wright. To their surprise, they found that the message was genuine.

" 'What hath God wrought!' " they repeated.

From then on, the value of the telegraph began to be recognized. Morse was honored not only in the United States but in Europe as well. The Queen of Spain presented him with a Cross of the Order of Isabella, the King of Prussia with a jeweled snuffbox; Napoleon III of France admitted him into the Legion of Honor; and the Sultan of Turkey decorated him with the Order of Glory. A statue of him was erected in Central Park, New York. And ten European countries awarded him 400,000 francs (about $80,000) for his great achievement in uniting nations in thought in a way never before imagined.

IV

Professor Morse's new experiment worked. He could send telegraph messages across water. This he had proved by laying a telegraph cable in New York harbor.

But he dreamed even a greater vision. "Man will not be satisfied to stop here," he prophesied. "Telegraph cables will some day connect Europe and America. Startling as this may now seem, I am confident the time will come when it will happen."

Ten years later he received a letter from a man who was to carry out this project. A certain Cyrus W. Field asked him if one could telegraph over a distance so great as that from Europe to America. Mr. Field had just been told of a scheme to connect Newfoundland to New York by telegraph cable.

"An interesting project," Field had thought. "I shall help to build it."

Later, when Field was standing in his library before a large globe of the earth, an idea flashed into his mind. "If we can connect the United States to Newfoundland by cable, why need we stop there? Cannot the telegraph link continents, the New World to the Old? In a few seconds a message from London might be able to reach New York. . . . I must find out if an electric current can travel such distances. If it can," he resolved, "there shall be an Atlantic cable."

He persuaded his friends, much against their will, to invest money in his idea.

"A fantastic scheme," they told him.

"A foolish plan."

"I am sure it will be a failure."

"Suppose you do not succeed," people asked him. "Suppose you make the attempt and fail. Your cable is lost at the bottom of the ocean. What will you do then?"

"Go to work to lay another," was his prompt answer. The idea so stirred his blood that he knew he could succeed.

One can scarcely picture a more difficult task. The ocean bottom, from two to six miles below the surface of the ocean, has its plateaus and valleys. And the slender cord to connect Europe and America was to consist of only seven fine copper wires twisted together.

Misfortune seemed to follow the ships that laid the cable. Again and again the wire cord would snap, and once when the cable broke, 144 miles of it was lost in the depths of the ocean.

To Cyrus Field, however, this only meant greater effort. Finally, on August 16, 1858, the telegraph cable flashed its first message across the Atlantic Ocean: "Europe and America are united by telegraph. Glory to God in the highest; on earth peace, and good will toward men."

The cable, alas, broke again, but Mr. Field did not lose heart. Finally, in 1866, his work was triumphant. Since then cable communication with Europe has been uninterrupted. Not only Field's dream but that of all mankind came true.

Alexander Graham Bell

(1847–1922)

THE VOICE FROM AFAR

I

"A-aa-aaa-AA . . . E-ee-eee-EE . . . O-oo-ooo-OO . . ."
Thus the matter really began.

"Gott im Himmel! Something dreadful is happening in Professor Helmholtz's laboratory. Come!" So thought the caretakers and students in the University of Heidelberg, as they passed through the corridors.

"Ee-yow-w-OO . . ."
Evidently somebody was in pain. No, it did not seem to be the professor howling. It sounded rather like the voice of a student.

But in the laboratory all was peace, if not quiet. The young teacher, Hermann von Helmholtz, was there, busy as usual, at a strange machine. He touched a screw. Something in the machine began to vibrate.

"Ah-ah-ah . . ." it wailed.

Helmholtz pushed a knob. *"Oo-oo-oo!!"* cried the machine, as if it were surprised.

"Excuse me, Dr. Helmholtz," said one of the spectators. "Your engine seems to have deep feelings."

"It is a sound machine," replied Helmholtz gravely.

"With it I am learning to imitate all kinds of tones. Just now I am working on the human voice."

"The next thing he'll want to do is make a tree," muttered an incredulous hearer.

"It is really a simple machine," explained Helmholtz. "Just a tuning fork vibrating, as it would if you struck it on a table."

"Is that what produces the tone?"

"Certainly. Anything — a string, a piece of metal, a sliver of wood — if it vibrates fast enough gives out a sound. That's what sound is — quivers in the air. A violinist makes a string vibrate with a bow, a singer makes his vocal chords vibrate by breathing air over them. Look here!" Helmholtz held up in his hand a piece of wire with a sort of cup at each end. "This will show you what I mean. If I pull this wire taut and speak into one of these cups, you will hear my voice come out of the other cup. Why? The sounds I utter are just quiverings of my vocal chords, rapid ones, of course; in fact, about a hundred and twenty every second. Well, these quivers pass on to the air in the cup and strike the bottom, which is made of a very light metal. So the bottom of this cup, in turn, vibrates, and makes the wire vibrate . . ."

"I see," said somebody eagerly, "and so the wire vibrates along its length to our ear at the other cup."

"Exactly!" concluded Helmholtz. "Your eardrum quivers, and the nerves inside pass the message to your brain."

No one doubted the word of Professor Helmholtz, for although he was young, he was already world-famous.

Even as a schoolboy, he had had a scientist's habits. His mother could never forget that once Hermann read that strong acid would eat holes in any fabric. "Do you think this is true?" asked his chum. "I don't know. We could make some acid and see. I know where my mother keeps the tablecloths," brightly suggested Hermann. And he led the way to his mother's store of precious linens. The experiment was a success, but the linen was ruined.

"Father, when I grow up," the boy one day announced, "I shall want to study science. I want to know why things happen as they do."

"Very well, my son," was his father's reply, "but you must earn your livelihood at the same time. Choose a profession — medicine, for instance. It is a science, for you will study the human body, and yet it will enable you to earn your living."

Young Helmholtz therefore studied physiology, and with such enthusiasm that he began to make discoveries which attracted the notice of the learned men of Germany. He did not practice medicine long, however, for universities felt honored if they could secure him to lecture to their students.

And then this modest professor astounded the world by writing one of the greatest books of all time on the marvel of the human eye, *Physiological Optics*, explaining how we see, and the mysteries of color and light, of shadows and bright images.

For recreation, Helmholtz turned to music. Nothing delighted him more than to play on the piano the sonatas of Mozart and Beethoven. Nothing pained him more than a false note.

"Why do some sounds please us," he wondered, "while others do not?"

That wonder caused Helmholtz to study sound, and finally to write a wonderful book, *The Sensations of Tone*.

II

In a noisy shop, in one of Boston's side streets, a tall young man was toiling seriously over a queer plaything. The June heat and the grime of the shop had so smeared his face that he, Professor Bell, the teacher of elocution and of speech to the deaf, was beyond recognition. And, truth to tell, he was not at all anxious to be seen or recognized. His rich friends Thomas Sanders and Gardiner Hubbard had warned him not to "fool" with this absurd dream of making sound travel over a wire. And how absurd a dream it was!

"Now, your other invention is worthwhile," Sanders had said. "Why not give your whole time to it? I mean that machine that will make it possible to *see* sound."

Bell, out of pity, was devoting his life to teaching the deaf and dumb how to speak and hear, and at the early age of twenty-five was already one of the world's greatest teachers of this art. He had come to America because his delicate health could not stand the trying climate of Scotland. All might have gone well with him had he continued as a teacher. Boston University had given him a professorship. Private pupils came from far and near.

It was then supposed that deaf people could not

speak because their speech organs were defective. Few persons understood that speech is acquired by imitation. Bell explained that most deaf children are mute only because they cannot hear.

He had brought to Boston the "Visible Speech" which his father had invented. His father, a professor of the art of speech, had worked out a system of writing sounds by drawing symbols to show the shapes taken by the lips and the positions of the tongue in uttering different sounds. This enabled one to know just how to manage his tongue, teeth and lips.

In teaching his classes, Bell would sketch the profile of a man on the blackboard, and add lines to illustrate the vocal chords and the tongue. His pupils learned to decipher the symbols readily, and reproduce the positions with their own speech organs. In this way they made the correct sounds, and they learned to speak.

All might have gone well — but Bell had seen a vision.

Sound — the waves of sound — could be seen with the eye! This vision had haunted him day and night, until he felt obliged to give up his teaching to invent some boon for the unfortunate deaf-mute, who would thereby be enabled to see the sounds which make human speech.

He took a light reed. One end of it touched a piece of smoked glass. The other end was attached to the inner portion of a human ear cut complete from the skull of a dead body. Into the ear this dreamy professor, with his pale face and black eyes, had whispered and shouted. And the drum of the ear had sent the current of his

voice through the heavy inner bone, setting the reed a-
quiver so that it made a kind of scrawl on the smoked
glass. What ghastly joy had he felt then!

All might yet have gone well had Bell not seen another vision.

"If this tiny disc of an eardrum can cause bone to
vibrate, why cannot an iron disc do the same to a wire?"
Why not indeed? He pictured two iron discs, joined by
an electric wire, and sounds at one end being carried
swiftly to the other.

He put aside his "visible speech" idea. Someone had
told him about the work of Helmholtz, and he began to
study it with great enthusiasm.

"Now this is too bad!" protested Sanders. "If you expect me to keep lending you money for food or shelter,
you'll have to give up this crazy idea of wire-talking."

"You must abandon your foolish telephone," said
Hubbard. "This wild dream you have of sending
speech over an electric wire — throw it out of your
mind!"

Bell faced these attacks bravely. He was poor, much
poorer than his friends knew. Yet — he would give up
all for science, and for the chance of making people
happier than they were. "If I can teach a deaf-mute to
talk," he thought determinedly, "perhaps I can find a
way to teach iron to talk."

For three years he stumbled along with only his vision to sustain him until, on this hot June afternoon,
his foolish toy looked like a sort of harmonica with a
springy steel reed, a magnet, and a wire.

Thomas A. Watson, his assistant, was in another
room — at the other end of the wire — with the same

sort of springy reed. Bell was bending, careworn and tired, over his wire.

Suddenly, a twang! For an instant Bell failed to comprehend. He was stunned. His ear had grown dull with months of waiting for this sound, and now — surely it had come! He rushed into the next room.

"Snap that reed again, Watson," he cried.

There was no mistake. It had come.

Of course the instrument could not do much yet. It could only squeak and buzz. But it was a great beginning. For Bell, as an electrician, had proved that an electrified wire could carry the vibrations of sound.

His next task was to make it useful to humanity — enable it to speed up industry, to gladden the lonely farmhouse . . .

For forty weeks he and Watson toiled. What were the best discs? Iron, copper; thin, thick; large, small; round, curved . . . ? All had to be tried. And what wire . . . ? And the best way to connect the wires . . . ?

Then one day Watson rushed from his receiver up two flights of stairs to the room where Bell was bending doubtfully over his instrument.

"I could hear you!" shouted Watson breathlessly. "I could hear your voice! You said: 'Mr. Watson, come here; I want you.' "

III

On his twenty-ninth birthday Bell obtained his patent. But so far only his few friends knew of his invention.

"You ought to make it public," advised his friends. "There may be something in it."

It happened luckily that the Centennial Exposition in Philadelphia was about to open just then, and Bell's friends thought it would be a good plan to exhibit the invention there.

Bell listened politely but gave the suggestion no thought. His friends knew that he was not interested in money or fame, and they began to fear that he would let this opportunity go by.

"What was the use of inventing this contraption," they urged, "if the world isn't going to use it? You must take it to the Exposition."

After much persuasion, Bell at last packed up his telephone and was off for Philadelphia.

But there a strange thing happened. As Bell stood proudly by the little table on which his telephone was arranged, no one paid the slightest attention to him. We today, who could afford to part with almost anything better than the telephone, marvel that the new telephone could have been passed by as lightly as a new kind of sulphur match or a new parer with which to skin potatoes. Past and around the little table the crowds swirled, with scarcely a glance at the tall pale young man who, on that sweltering day, was cold with fear and bitterness.

Sunday came. It was to be the big day. Their Majesties the Emperor and Empress of Brazil were expected. Lord Kelvin, the great English scientist, was to attend. And the anxious Bell expected the judges to consider his invention.

The hot day went by while Bell was torn with anxiety and restraint. At last, about seven o'clock, the judges gave Bell his turn. Everyone was hot and tired, and the judges meant to give Bell only a moment, feeling it was their duty to pay him some attention. One picked up the receiver, stared dumbly at it — and put it down. Another laughed and turned away.

Suddenly there swept into the room the regal party, His Royal Highness the Emperor Dom Pedro de Alcantara. Both hands outstretched, Dom Pedro advanced to Bell. "Professor Bell, I am delighted to see you again."

His heart throbbing, Bell recognized the benevolent man who had once visited his speech class in Boston. The judges were impressed. Their indifference changed to respect as they watched the attention the Emperor gave to Bell and his strange invention.

Quickly a wire was strung across the room. At one end, the Emperor placed the attached instrument to his ear. To the other end Bell marched, and put his mouth to the instrument there. What would happen? All eyes were riveted on the face of the monarch. Suddenly a look of utter amazement swept Dom Pedro's face. In bewilderment, he lifted his head and exclaimed, "My God, it talks!"

Lord Kelvin approached, the world's foremost electrical scientist. He and his wife ran from one end of the wire to the other, like a pair of delighted children, to speak and to hear.

"It is the most wonderful thing I have seen in America," he declared.

The judges became enthusiastic. This little instrument became the star of the Exposition. As it had been neglected, everything else was now neglected for it. Shortly universities spread their honors before Alexander Bell, and the world its wealth. But the young inventor felt that his real glory lay in his work with deafmutes.

And then followed what even Bell himself did not foresee. The telephone became the nerves of the nation. If the telephone were suddenly swept out of existence, much of our industry would have to check its stride, would shrivel and lapse back into the slow pace of the years before Bell invented the telephone.

Bell once described an inventor as "a man who looks around upon the world, and is not content with things as they are; he wants to improve whatever he sees; he wants to benefit the world; he is haunted by an idea; the spirit of invention possesses him, seeking materialization."

This description fits Alexander Graham Bell perfectly.

Thomas Alva Edison

(1847–1931)

THE WIZARD OF MENLO PARK

I

FROM the Boston boat there landed in New York in the year 1869 a young man of twenty-two, penniless. The passage money had taken his last cent.

As he walked up the street from the wharf, he passed a warehouse of tea, in which he saw a tea taster at work. "Perhaps he will give me a cup," thought the youth. He walked in and asked the taster for a cup of tea, which was given him. This was Thomas Edison's first breakfast in New York.

Now to find his friend. He had once known a telegraph operator who was now in New York and who, Edison hoped, would help him find a job. After a considerable search he found his man. But he, too, was looking for work, and he could lend Edison only a dollar.

The tired, hungry Edison, with a dollar in his pocket, at once hurried to a restaurant. "Apple dumplings and coffee," he ordered. He never enjoyed a meal more.

But he must find work! He was an experienced telegraph operator, so he went to the Western Union. But they did not need any additional men. For the next few days he wandered the streets, seeking work — but everywhere he was rejected.

Somehow he got permission to sleep in the battery room of the Gold and Stock Telegraph Company, a concern transmitting stock quotations. One day, when he was sitting in their office wondering where next he could turn for a job, something suddenly went wrong with the whole system. About three hundred messenger boys came rushing up the stairs, all shouting at once that the indicators, which were worked by telegraphy, were out of order.

Dr. Laws, the vice-president of the company, rushed in, frantic. Every expert he could find he put on the job, but they only seemed to get in each other's way. Nobody seemed to know what to do.

Edison had meanwhile studied the machine. He turned to Dr. Laws. "Dr. Laws," he timidly ventured, "I believe I can locate the difficulty."

"Fix it! Fix it! But be quick," shouted the excited man.

Edison examined the mechanism again. A broken spring he found had fallen between the wheels. Soon the instruments were working as well as before.

Dr. Laws now invited Edison into his office. For some time Dr. Laws talked, and at length offered Edison the job of manager of the entire plant at a salary of three hundred dollars a month. The youth almost collapsed.

With so much money he could open a workshop for his spare time. That was happiness. Not only did Edison open his workshop, where he experimented with electricity, but the first fruit of his spare time was the invention for the Gold and Stock Telegraph Company of a much better machine than the one they were using.

That caused the president of the company to send for Edison. "How much do you want for your invention?" the president asked.

Edison had thought of asking five thousand dollars for it. But now, face to face with the president, he lost courage. "Perhaps I ought to ask three thousand," he thought, "for he won't give me as much as five."

"I would rather have you make the offer, General Lefferts," he managed to stammer.

"How would forty thousand dollars strike you?"

Edison opened his mouth in astonishment. So much? But General Lefferts misunderstood. He thought Edison was not satisfied. "That is all we can afford to give, Mr. Edison."

Edison nodded. He would accept the offer.

When he signed the agreement, he was given a check for forty thousand dollars. This was the first check he had ever received.

He rushed to the bank. The bank clerk, thinking to play a joke on the youth, gave him the money in bills of five- and ten-dollar denominations. Laboriously Edison stowed them away in every pocket. All that night he sat up, fearing that his money might be stolen. For two days he carried it around with him, until at last a friend persuaded him to open a bank account.

II

Yet this lad had had only three months' schooling!

In those three months, however, he had distinguished himself. He had been at the foot of the class! "He is 'addled'," his teacher said.

When his mother heard this, she took him away from school. The schoolmaster had forced him to learn by rote. She knew her son better. He was always learning with his interminable questions, why? She had been a school teacher herself, so she decided to teach him at home. There he made such rapid progress that he was soon reading books like Gibbon's *Decline and Fall of the Roman Empire* — and that is not light reading.

But mainly he was interested in experiments. He began to challenge and test statements that he read in books on science. For instance, he read that if you fill a balloon with gas, it rises. This gave him an idea. If a person were filled with gas, he could then fly. To test this theory, he coaxed a boy who worked for the family to swallow a large quantity of Seidlitz powders, assuring him that if he did so, he would certainly be able to fly. Somehow the experiment failed. Instead of flying, the boy became so sick that a doctor had to be called.

Nor did this discourage young Thomas. He kept right on experimenting. In the cellar of their house, in Port Huron, Michigan, he made his first laboratory. Two hundred bottles were there, all labeled "Poison."

"My mother's ideas and mine differ at times," he said, "especially when I get to experimenting and muss up things."

Since his pocket money was not sufficient to buy all the chemicals he wanted, he convinced his parents that they should permit him to earn some extra money. Soon he was selling newspapers on the Grand Trunk Railway line.

For another scientist, selling newspapers on a train might have meant absence from his laboratory. Not so with Edison. It only meant that his experiments were now conducted, not only in the cellar but also in the baggage car of the train. There he kept his bottles, test tubes, and batteries. There he even read his books on chemistry, testing every statement in them.

The train left at seven in the morning. When it returned at nine-thirty in the evening, Edison would continue his experiments, which lasted until all hours of the night. Yet he found time to run a paper, the *Weekly Herald,* of which he was editor, reporter, advertising manager, and news agent.

One day, while he was standing on the railroad platform, he noticed a child playing on the tracks. Just then a freight train came hurtling down. There was not a second to lose. Dashing across the tracks, Edison pulled the child to safety just as the train rushed by. The child's father, who was the station master, rewarded Edison in the only way he could — by offering to teach him telegraphy.

For three months Edison studied during his spare time with this station master. Then his teacher declared that he was ready to "graduate." Thomas Edison now became a telegraph operator — soon the fastest operator employed by the Western Union. But he never ceased to experiment with his bottles and wires and

batteries. Then one memorable day he bought Michael
Faraday's book, *Experimental Researches in Electricity.*
His day's work at the telegraph office was not over until
late at night. Then began his reading of Faraday's
book. He not only read the words but also repeated the
experiments. For in Michael Faraday he had found his
hero, the scientist whom he wished most to emulate.

III

We are now so used to the phonograph that for us it
has ceased to be a wonder. But not until Thomas Edison invented it had anyone even dreamed that it was
possible to hear again and again a sound after it had
once been uttered. "Why," people would say, "you
might as well try to capture the howl of the wind!"
They laughed at the mention of a machine, mere pieces
of metal, which would repeat singing and speaking as
they had sounded in life! Edison, however, believed the
wonders of nature had not been exhausted.

One day he gave John Kreusi, his cleverest mechanic, a rough sketch of a machine and asked him to
build a model.

"What is this going to be?" asked Kreusi.

"A machine that will talk," calmly replied Edison.

Although Kreusi had seen Edison do wonderful
things, yet this was too much. "Impossible!" He shook
his head. "This experiment will be a failure."

Nevertheless he went back to the factory and worked.
After thirty hours he smilingly brought a large clumsy
machine to Edison.

The men in the factory gathered around. The foreman of the machine shop offered to bet Edison a box of cigars that it would not work. "Taken!" said the wizard.

The strange-looking machine was set up on the table. The workmen gathered about. Thomas Edison now slowly turned the handle of the shaft and in a loud voice declaimed, "Mary had a little lamb . . ." The workmen tittered.

Then Edison put a needle down at the starting place of his declamation and again turned the handle. Out of the machine, faintly but distinctly, came the voice of Edison, reciting, "Mary had a little lamb . . ."

"*Mein Gott im Himmel!*" cried John Kreusi.

The rest were awed. They could not utter a word. But the foreman broke the spell by saying. "Well, I guess I lost." Then they all joined hands and danced around Edison, singing and shouting. They knew it was a memorable event in the history of man's progress.

The next day all New York was in great excitement. "Edison has invented a machine that talks!" people told each other. The railway ran special trains to his laboratory at Menlo Park, New Jersey. The place was thronged with visitors. Many suspected fraud, but when they heard their own voices come from the phonograph box, they were convinced.

Edison, however, did not rest. He worked for perfection. Not until the phonograph had recorded Beethoven's *Ninth Symphony* did Edison think he had done all that he could with it. The poet Tennyson wished for "the sound of a voice that is still"; and Edison realized the wish.

IV

The man to whom more than to any one else we owe the comforts of electricity is Thomas Alva Edison.

We press a button — and we have summoned the mightiest of jinn, electricity, to do our bidding. We say to this jinn, "Let us have light," and the electric lamp glows.

Little did Sir Humphry Davy dream, when he produced the arc light in 1812, that this electric lighting would some day have banished candles and gas lighting, and would bring about most wonderful changes in the world. To Sir Humphry Davy the electric light was only one more of his curious experiments — just for the sake of scientific knowledge. To Thomas Edison it was a challenge. It seemed to beckon him. And he continued this strange experiment of Davy in order to play with it, to study it, for it whispered in his ear, "I am a jinn. I can serve humanity." Edison listened to this voice — and the result is the incandescent lamp and his system for distributing electric light, electric heat, and electric power.

Edison felt that before he would be ready to tackle this problem, he must study gas lighting. Therefore, he read all he could upon that subject. Soon there were few gas engineers who knew the subject of gas lighting more thoroughly. Then he felt ready. He saw that the electric light must be simple to manage and not too expensive, and that it must be so arranged that every light on a circuit could be extinguished or lighted independently of the other lights on that circuit — a scheme which engineers said could not be achieved.

To produce a glowing in the lamp, he first tried sticks of paper tissue coated with lampblack and tar. These burners lasted only ten or fifteen minutes and were therefore not suitable. Edison then tried wires made of platinum and iridium.

At this time he and his whole staff worked hard. His men worked day and night, with only four to six hours' sleep. A midnight supper became the rule. Then they would relax and sing and be jolly. Had you come into the Edison laboratory at night, you might have found one or two of the men sleeping on one of the laboratory tables, the rest busily working. Edison himself would be working, working, till three or four in the morning. He then would lie down on one of the tables, and with nothing but a book or two for a pillow, fall into a sound sleep.

At first results seemed discouraging. Edison had hooked up several lamps with platinum burners. The current was turned on. For a moment there was a dim light. "A little more juice, Kreusi," said Edison. Then followed an explosion — and darkness.

People heard what Edison was trying to do. They forgot the wonders he had accomplished; they called him "dreamer," and many wrote to the newspapers, calling him a fool. Yet for thirteen months he continued to experiment, never wearying, always searching for the right materials to be used inside the glass bulb. Other men would have quit long before, and we might still be reading by gas and candle. But Edison was always cheerful, knowing he was on the right track. "What other people called failures — these," said he, "taught me what not to do."

Once he sent for a spool of cotton sewing thread. His assistants looked doubtful. How could so frail a thing stand an electric current that melted the hardest of metals? Edison took a short piece of the thread, bent it into horseshoe shape, and placed it in a nickel mold. This he baked in a furnace for five hours.

When the mold was cooled and opened, the next task was to withdraw the delicate carbon thread, and seal it in a glass bulb. All that night, the next day, and the next night, for Edison and his men there was neither sleep nor rest. From a whole spool of cotton, they finally succeeded in getting just one piece that did not break when taken from the mold.

"Batchelor, my assistant," says Edison, "took up the precious carbon, and I marched after him, as if guarding a mighty treasure. To our consternation, just as we reached the bench, the carbon thread broke. We turned to the main laboratory and set to work again. It was late in the afternoon before we had produced another carbon thread, which was again broken by a screw driver falling against it. But we turned back again and, before night, the carbon was completed and inserted in the lamp. The bulb was exhausted of air and sealed, the current turned on, and the sight we had so long desired to see met our eyes."

He had made the light.

For forty hours it burned.

Edison then began to dream of electricity as lighting the streets and the homes. What was the best material of which to make a carbon thread? He carbonized everything he could lay his hands on — cocoanut shells, twine, tissue paper, celluloid, cardboard. Nothing in the laboratory escaped his experiments. Umbrellas and walking sticks mysteriously vanished. He even plucked hair from the red beard of Mackenzie, the man who taught him telegraphy. In search of material he sent men to China, to the Amazon, and up the Rio de la Plata, to the West Indies, to British Guiana, Ceylon, and India. At last, in Japan, was found a bamboo fiber which, when carbonized, glowed in the glass bulb to Edison's satisfaction. Today filaments of tungsten are used.

This most remarkable inventor will live in the world's history not only for these wonders, each of which is enough to immortalize any man, but for many others. He invented a motion-picture machine and helped develop the "talkies"; he invented the mimeograph; he improved the storage battery, the telephone, dynamos, electric trains; he invented machines for making cement, and many labor-saving devices.

One of America's great gifts to civilization was Thomas Alva Edison.

Guglielmo Marconi

(1874–1937)

TO THE UTTERMOST
ENDS OF THE EARTH

I

To YOUNG Marconi of Bologna there were no greater
heroes than the men of science; no adventures more
thrilling than theirs. He would try to fill his own life
with such adventures, he determined. He felt, though,
that all the great things had been done already. Nothing was left. Or if there was something still to invent or
discover, some great man would do it soon.

But no! "There will always be an opportunity to
make inventions or discoveries," Professor Augusto
Righi told him. "Who ever dreamed a hundred years
ago that a conversation would pass between people
miles apart? Who ever imagined that a voice or a message would be carried on a wire? Some day, perhaps, we
shall send messages even without the help of wires."

The most marvelous thing that Professor Righi
showed Marconi happened with two coils of wire. They
were put some distance apart. He repeated an experiment of Heinrich Hertz for the eager youth. Guglielmo
Marconi was astounded.

"The Hertzian waves sent out by the transmitter

cause the sparking in the receiver," explained Righi. "Soon we may not need Morse's telegraph or Bell's telephone, which depend on wires to carry our messages." Young Marconi had felt that soon one of the heroes of science would invent a *wireless* telegraph. One day it flashed into his mind that if no one else would invent a wireless telegraph, he himself might try. True, he was young — only nineteen — but he was also ambitious. He began to study all about these wonderful electric waves. He devoured every scientific book that fell into his hands.

His father encouraged him; gave him the garden to experiment in and funds with which to buy his wire, poles, string, tin, and whatever else he needed. The poles he buried at opposite sides of the garden. He had learned that with an earth connection he could increase the distance over which he could transmit his signals.

He connected a Morse telegraph key to his apparatus. When Marconi pressed the key, it caused the transmitter to spark. If he held down the key for several seconds, a dash of the spark occurred; if he just clicked it, a dot. He had attached a coherer, or detector, to the receiver on the opposite pole. As a result, his receiver could reproduce the dots and dashes. Young Marconi was able to send messages across the garden — without wires.

"But suppose there's a hill or a wall between my poles. What will happen then?" he thought anxiously. He tried the experiment. He set his poles up in the fields, with a hill between and several walls. The electric wave went right through the hill and the walls.

But he was not yet satisfied with his invention. "The

signals I receive must be clear," he determined. "I need a more sensitive coherer for catching these faint electromagnetic waves." Many more experiments followed, until at last he had improved his device and had learned to "tune in" these waves.

Soon he could signal eight miles away!

He announced his invention to the world. The world greeted him as it had greeted Bell and Morse before him. It laughed and scoffed. "You are exaggerating slightly," it said with sarcasm. "Do you mean that these waves go through rocks? At the most you have only a toy. It can never be of any real use."

"Toy!" said Marconi. "This invention will connect continent with continent. It will save lives . . ."

He did not boast. He made the wireless do both.

II

"Your system works well for short distances," he was told, "but it can never be made to serve for great lengths. The earth curves. Somehow that will stop you."

Marconi planned a great test. For distance he would use the width of the Atlantic Ocean. On one shore was a transmitting station with its huge antenna surrounded by a ring of masts 200 feet high. On the opposite shore, beyond 1700 miles of curving ocean, a 400-foot wire antenna was to be kept aloft by a kite. Some one would tap the telegraph key in the Old World, and the click would be heard in the New World. . . .

Very quietly he sailed for America and landed at St. John's, Newfoundland, on December 6, 1901. Before

he left England, he had instructed his assistants there at
Poldhu, the southwestern tip of Cornwall, to signal at a
certain hour each day the letter S, three dots in the
Morse code.

The first day for the signal was December 12. At
Poldhu, a group of men had crowded about the "sending set."

"Is it time?" asked the operator anxiously.

"Right."

The operator released the key.

Marconi described what happened 1700 miles away.
In Newfoundland the day was raw and bleak. "I was
standing in a bitter-cold room on the top of a hill in
Newfoundland wondering if I should be able to hear
the simple letter S transmitted from England . . . In
spite of a raging gale, we flew a kite carrying an aerial
some four hundred feet long. About twelve-thirty in
the afternoon a succession of three faint clicks, corre-
sponding to the prearranged signal, sounded definitely
and distinctly in the telephone held at my ear. This
could only be that the electric waves sent out had traversed the seventeen hundred miles of the Atlantic un-
impeded."

The world heard and doubted. It was at length convinced, however, and when it was not pressing its
honors upon him, it kept Marconi busy building wireless stations the earth over.

Marconi now turned his attention to the preserva-
tion of human life. "If ships had wireless sets, they
could signal for help in distress."

On board the good ship *Philadelphia* he fitted out a
new kind of wireless — one that printed on a tape the

message it received. He tried it out one day for the first
time in the captain's cabin. The chief officer happened
to step into the room just at the crucial moment. He
saw with his own eyes a message from Poldhu being
written out. Excitedly he rushed from the cabin and
about the ship, telling all of the marvel.

Everyone laughed. "Do you want us to believe that?"
they asked.

"Go and see," said the officer.

They crowded into the cabin. *"Tap, tap, tap,"*
sounded the inker as it clicked its message on the tape.
Marconi smiled as he noticed the amazed stares.

If Guglielmo Marconi had saved a human life from
drowning, he would have been given a medal for heroism. How much more then is he a hero that by his invention he has saved scores of human beings from death
in the sea?

The first boatload of people to owe gratitude to him
were the passengers and crew of the liner *Republic*.
One dark night in 1903, off the port of New York, this
ship suddenly collided with another, the *Florida*. In a
few moments the water was rushing through a hole in
the side of the *Republic*. The ship was sinking. It was a
simple matter of a moment to send a wireless S O S, the
signal meaning distress. The *Florida* was doing all it
could. But the electric messenger brought aid from all
sides, and the passengers and the crew were saved.

For these and for other inventions Italy had made
Marconi a senator, and the Nobel Prize was his. Marconi had shown us that the world is a close family, and
that no land is too distant for our words to reach it.

The Wright Brothers

Wilbur Wright *(1867–1912)*
Orville Wright *(1871–1948)*

MEN WITH WINGS

I

THE story is told that in ancient Greece lived Daedalus, a famous mechanic, and his son Icarus. Once, when the two were far from home visiting Crete, King Minos clapped them in prison. Seeking a means of escape over the vast sea, Daedalus fashioned wax wings for himself and Icarus, and away they flew to Sicily. Daedalus fared safely, but unhappily Icarus soared too near the sun. The wax melted, and down he plunged into the sea . . .

Every age has told a story like this, because there have always been men wistful to fly. Some dreamed of floating lazily on a cloud, while others envied the wings of the bird. Both dreams have come true — although both came strangely disguised. He who wishes to float through the air may do so today in a glider, and the wings of a jet aircraft will take man anywhere faster than the wings of the strongest bird.

We must thank the Montgolfier brothers for making the dream of floating in the air come true. In the little town of Annonay, France, there still stands the paper mill that was theirs. But life held for them many more interesting things than paper mills — chimney smoke, for instance.

"Stephen, just see how eagerly the smoke ascends," said Joseph to his brother, as they sat before the fireplace, watching the smoldering logs. "I was thinking," he continued, "that since the smoke rises with so much force, perhaps we can get it to carry something up with it. Up above, it would float like a cloud."

Stephen was silent for a moment. "If we could capture a cloud, and put it in a bag, the bag would float. The bag would defy the pull of the earth."

"We can't do that. How could we reach the cloud? But I'll tell you what we can do. Let's catch the smoke of the chimney in a bag."

For the next six months, at odd moments, they made their bag "to catch smoke." Wisely they kept the idea secret, knowing well that the villagers would laugh if they heard of such a foolish plan. The bag was made of linen and blown up. The bottom of the linen bag they purposely left open.

In the middle of November, 1782, they were ready for their great test. Under the opening of the bag, Joseph Montgolfier put some burning paper. Smoke entered the bag. And as the bag filled with the smoke, it rose to the ceiling of the room.

"Smoke does carry the bag up," cried Stephen. "Let's try it again, under the open sky."

There, to their delight, the linen bag rose seventy feet high. And when it finally fell, it descended very gently.

People heard the strange news, and scoffed. The

brothers therefore decided to make larger bags, and with these convince the world of their discovery. They invited all to see their new balloon. The crowd that came to laugh at the brothers who could make things float in the air stood in amazement when the balloon shot six thousand feet into the air.

When the great news reached Paris, the scientists there invited the brothers to repeat their experiment in the French capital. These learned men — among whom was Benjamin Franklin — stood with bated breath as they watched the balloon rise.

The greatest triumph for the Montgolfier brothers came when the King of France wished them to repeat their experiment before the entire court of France. On this occasion the balloon carried the first passengers of the air — a sheep, a rooster, and a duck.

II

"If a bird can master the air, why can't we?" thought other dreamers. But the daring ones who tried were usually killed and cited as warnings to other rash souls.

To Otto Lilienthal in Pomerania, Germany, the fate of other men was not a warning. "No wonder we failed," he said. "We know too little about the laws of flying. First we must watch the birds."

For a long time he watched these creatures which glide about in the air so easily. "How does the wind lift a bird's wings?" was the question he studied. No one before had ever watched birds as thoroughly as Lilienthal did. He made hundreds of sketches of a bird's wings in various positions — when the bird begins to fly, when it rises, when it soars, and when it lands. For twenty years he continued his bird study. At the end of that time he was ready to build a machine which would make man a rival of the bird. There was no need for guesswork; he knew exactly how he ought to build it.

In 1891 the world had a shock. With its own eyes it saw a man gliding through the air on tremendous wings. He looked like a gigantic bat hovering aloft. The legend of Daedalus had come true.

"Man can fly. All he needs is practice," said Lilienthal, as he thrust his arms through padded tubes and held fast to a crossbar. Once the gliding machine was firmly attached, he was ready to leap from a hill into the air.

He could glide as much as a hundred yards, and learned to soar as well. To steer himself, he tried moving his body about — forward, backward, or from side to side. "I need more practice," he thought. "When I can balance myself as well as a cyclist who controls his wheel, I shall have won."

After a fashion, Lilienthal did win, for he learned to turn a complete circle and to stay poised in the air like a gull. Five years of practice and more than two thousand flights in his glider made Lilienthal an expert.

"I am now ready to try a motor in my glider," he said to his friends.

He built a new flying machine, into which he put a small motor. Then, one summer day, he took off, a large crowd watching him. For a few moments he soared. Then came a sudden lull in the wind. Some-

thing went wrong with the motor. Like Icarus, Lilienthal fell.

III

The newsboy had left a paper, as usual, at the
Wright Cycle Company in Dayton, Ohio.

Wilbur Wright, a large man with gray eyes and a
long aquiline nose, glanced through the paper. "What's
this!" he exclaimed, as he turned to his brother Orville.
"The flying man killed!"

Orville looked up from his work. Wilbur continued:
"Berlin, August 12 — Herr Otto Lilienthal, an engineer, who for many years experimented with the building of flying machines, met with an accident that resulted in his death . . ."

As he prolonged the reading about Lilienthal, both
brothers became greatly interested. Deeply impressed
by Lilienthal's work, they sent to Berlin for a copy of
his book.

The book came. "It's in German," they said disap-
pointedly. They could only look at the pictures. But
within a short time they had learned enough German to
understand the book thoroughly.

They liked the way Lilienthal emphasized the idea
of constant practice. "Every bird is an acrobat," he
wrote. "Whoever would master the air must learn to
imitate the birds. We must fly and fall, and fall and fly,
until we can fly without falling."

From the time of Lilienthal's fall, Orville and Wilbur thought less and less of their bicycle business. The
lure of flying had seized them. They read all they could

about flying, and they began to watch the birds on the wing. If, when they were in their shop, one of the brothers spied a flock of birds flying by, "Birds!" he would shout. Both would drop their work, and rush to the window, gazing until the birds were out of sight.

For the rest of the day, during their spare time, they would argue about what they had seen — about how the bird soars, how its wings are shaped when out-stretched, how it balances. For days on end they talked about these matters.

"I'm right," Orville would say. "It's like this . . ."

"No, I'm right," Wilbur would insist. "It's like that . . ."

"Well," Orville would hesitate, "I guess you are right."

Wilbur would be silent for some moments. "No, Orville. I see that you have the better idea," he would finally admit. And they would laugh and go on happily.

They could hardly wait till Sunday afternoon. Then, for hours and hours, they would lie on their backs on a hill outside of Dayton, watching buzzards soar on the rising currents of air.

For five years they studied and argued about flying. They made tiny machines which they flew in the air like kites.

"I've figured it out," reflected one of the brothers. "Lilienthal, in five years, spent about five hours actually gliding in the air."

"The wonder," returned his brother, "is not that he accomplished so little, but that he accomplished so much."

"Imagine a bicycle rider attempting to ride through

crowded city streets after five hours of practice, spread out in bits of ten seconds over five years! Yet even with this brief practice, wasn't Lilienthal remarkably successful in overcoming the eddies in the gusts of wind? If we could only find some way by which we could practice by the hour instead of by the second, we could solve the problem . . ."

To this most dangerous of hobbies, they began to devote all their time and energy, for Wilbur and Orville were thorough mechanics and, in addition, were captivated by aeronautics.

IV

From the time when Wilbur was eleven years old and Orville seven, they had shown an interest in flying. It began in this way. Their father, Bishop Milton Wright, once walked into the room in which they were playing. His hand playfully concealed some object.

The boys were wondering what his hand hid, when he suddenly said, "Here's something for you," and into the air he tossed a whirring object.

"It flies," cried the boys, as they watched it spin across the room and strike the ceiling. There it fluttered about for a few moments before it fell. The boys jumped for the toy, now lying on the floor. They picked it up, and eagerly examined it.

"What is it?" asked Orville.

"A toy bat," suggested Wilbur.

"It's a helicopter," explained their father.

"How does it work?" they asked.

Bishop Wright therefore showed them that the "bat"

was only a cork and bamboo frame, covered with paper; that it rose in the air by means of some twisted rubber bands.

"Where did you get it, father?" asked Wilbur.

"I bought it when I was in New York. Not long ago there lived a certain Frenchman, who fell sick and became a cripple. Since the poor fellow could not walk, he began to dream of flying. That is how he came to invent this flying toy. Once he tried to make a real flying machine, but he failed. Finally everyone laughed at his ambitions, and he died of a broken heart."

The boys were silent for a moment. Then one exclaimed, "Perhaps some day a great man will succeed."

"Perhaps," replied their father.

Again and again they flew the toy. "I wonder if we can make it fly higher," said Wilbur.

"Let's make a bigger 'bat'," replied his brother. They did make another flying toy, somewhat larger, but this one did not fly as well as the one which their father had brought them.

"Perhaps we did not make our 'bat' right," they said. "We must try again." What puzzled them was that, although their toys would fly, the larger the toy, the less time it would stay up in the air. And beyond a certain size their "bat" would not fly at all.

Defeated, they turned their interest to kites, which would stay up in the air. But the helicopter always remained a vivid memory to the Wright brothers.

Several years later, young Orville, in company with a friend, decided to publish a newspaper. It was to consist of four pages. They called it the *Midget,* but the first issue was even smaller than its name implied. For, alas, they ran short of news. They solved the difficulty in a very novel way — they left page three blank.

Orville's father was given a copy of the *Midget*. "It is imperfect work," he commented, and he suppressed the entire edition.

Not at all abashed by the failure of the *Midget*, both brothers decided to publish another paper. Not having enough money to buy a press, they made one themselves. And one Saturday night the *West Side News* was delivered to as many as four hundred subscribers.

From printing, however, they soon turned to the craze of the day, bicycles. They set up a little shop for repairing and making wheels. They made their own tools, even such complicated ones as lathes.

Before long people began to know and like these quiet, pleasant brothers. Not only were their wheels well-made, but on them they installed a splendid safety brake which they had invented.

One day they thought of having a bit of fun. They rode all over town on a huge tandem bicycle they had built. It was made of two old high wheels, connected by a long gas pipe. "It's a better sight than seeing a circus," was the town's comment.

And then came the death of Lilienthal. The torch, which his helpless fingers let go, the brothers grasped to blaze the way to higher glories.

"Lilienthal was not on the right track when he shifted his body at every gust of wind to balance himself. It's both too difficult and too exhausting," said one brother.

"Yes, the wind often veers several times a second, much quicker than a man can think," agreed the other.

"But how can we get control? If I let a piece of paper fall, it doesn't swoop down straight. It turns over. The air resists it. How can we ride such an uncertain steed as an airplane and keep our balance?"

After much study, they concluded that if you could lie flat in the airplane instead of standing upright, as in Lilienthal's machine, the wind resistance could be reduced. And instead of the rider's shifting in the machine when he wanted to balance and to steer about, they decided that the machine should do this work. They put a rudder in front, and soon were able to control the airplane.

One day Octave Chanute appeared on the field. He was an old friend and they looked to him for counsel. He watched them leap and soar from spot to spot, grasshopper fashion, on their wings of wood and canvas. He carefully studied the gliding machine.

Octave Chanute was the greatest authority in America on the history of the flying machine. He, too, had been experimenting with flying machines.

"Do you young men know," he finally said, "that you have come nearer to the art of flying than any other man who ever lived?" Chanute was most encouraging, and the brothers worked with a harder will than ever.

On December 17, 1903, they were ready. A general invitation was sent to the people of Kitty Hawk, North Carolina, to come and watch the fliers. Only five people were willing to face the cold December wind to see a flying machine that would not fly, as they thought.

The machine was made ready. The engine which the brothers had to build themselves, for no company would undertake to construct one for them, was started. Orville Wright got in.

And then a miracle! The airplane rose and stayed in the air twelve seconds! For the first time in history, a machine carrying a man raised itself into the air *by its own power* and landed without being wrecked.

The myth of Daedalus had become reality.

BOOK IV

Heroes
of Biology and Medicine

William Harvey

(1578–1657)

BEGINNING OF
MODERN PHYSIOLOGY

I

As William Shakespeare lay in his bed in Stratford-on-Avon, a few days before his eyes shut forever, the historical curtain in another part of England arose on a startling scene.

It is in London, in the theater of the Royal College of Physicians. On the benches, inclined semicircularly one above the other, sits a curious throng — students, surgeons, officials of state, trustees of the college, and private citizens. All eyes are directed to a table in the center of the theater. On this table is stretched the corpse of a criminal, executed the day before. At either end of the table stands a "Master of the Anatomy," scalpel in hand, waiting to expose the structure of the body at the bidding of the chief actor in the scene.

He, the chief actor, is sitting opposite the center of the table. On his head is the cap denoting a doctor. He is a small, dark man with a round face and curly hair. His eyes are brilliantly black and full of spirit.

He holds a little wand with which he alternately gestures in the air and touches here and there the cadaver. By the sheer magnetism of his personality, he is making a powerful impression.

"In half an hour," his words flow with rapid earnestness, "the heart pumps out of its chambers more blood than is contained in the whole body. Whence does the heart get its inexhaustible supply? Where does it all go?"

The crowd stirs uneasily. This Harvey is a disturbing fellow. Why challenge a question that was settled and laid to rest long ago — by the revered Galen, by the great Aristotle?

"What line can you draw with your pencil, my fellow students, that has no end to it? A circle. How can the heart eject all the blood in the body without running dry in a half hour? There can be only one answer: by using the same blood over and over again."

In the assembly excitement runs rampant. The layman opens wide his eyes, the student's pencil glides briskly, the doctors appear to be scandalized as if fearful lest Aristotle and Galen are groaning in their graves.

"The blood circulates through the body." Impossible! Has the fellow no respect for the ancient masters of medicine and for the present beliefs?

"But, Dr. Harvey," someone implores, "Galen says that the blood travels through the body like people moving through the streets of a city." And another adds, "The divine Aristotle teaches that the blood is created from food in the liver which sends it to the heart. From the heart it is distributed by the veins through the body."

"The veins go *toward* the heart," Harvey calmly corrects, "and the arteries carry the blood *away* from that organ."

"Worse and worse! You mean the arteries actually carry blood?"

"Certainly."

"But we understand the arteries carry air or spirit."

"Look here," says William Harvey impatiently, indicating a chart, "I'll show the process to you; you shall see it with your very eyes. It is not mysterious. The heart dilates with blood. Then it contracts and squeezes the blood into the arteries. The heart's constant pumping causes the pulse beat which is heard.

"Notice the valves in the veins of the body. Nature has not placed them without design. This is the reason: to prevent the blood from flowing *into* the limbs *from* the heart. The valves, however, do permit free passage of blood *from* the limbs *toward* the heart. It is clear, therefore, that blood must be sent from the heart through the arteries and return through the veins."

He stops and gazes about him to see what effect his words have had. Surely he has proved to them that the blood circulates! They cannot refuse to believe their eyes! But on the faces of his fellow doctors he reads cold scorn and hostility. He is either slightly mad, they think, or a fool.

Well, then, he will debate no more with them. He flings down his wand contemptuously and, turning abruptly on his heel, strides angrily out of the theater.

II

When William Harvey was sixteen years old, he was admitted to Cambridge University. At that time he was able to read and write Latin and Greek, and converse in Latin.

His day at Cambridge began with chapel at five in the morning. The lectures were given from six to ten. Then a meager lunch at ten, following which he attended classes and studied texts. A sparse evening meal was followed by more study. In cold weather students generally exercised — they ran for half an hour — in order to raise their body heat before going to bed in an unheated room.

William Harvey heard of an Italian university which was unusual in that its professors did not rely solely on books. That seemed to Harvey to be just the place for him, because he believed in observing nature direct, not through a printed page. In 1599 he traveled to Italy where he enrolled in the University of Padua.

Here he observed and participated in doing experiments in biology. The school had an anatomical "theater." In a small oval in the middle of the room was a table for the body, or that part of it which was to be dissected. Around it were six concentric galleries in which the students stood to watch the dissection. So William Harvey was trained in the art and practice of medicine. When he returned to England, he continued to increase his knowledge mainly by direct observation and experiment. That was how he came to discover that the blood circulated through the body.

He did not announce his theory until he was sure he was right. Many a year had he spent studying the circulation of the blood, and in over forty different kinds of creatures — fishes, reptiles, birds, snails, crabs. Not until after that prolonged examination had he begun to apply his theory to human blood.

Nevertheless, his discovery of the circulation of the blood met with such opposition from the world's leading anatomists that more than twenty-five years passed before recognition came to him. Meanwhile people believed him crackbrained. Physicians derided him. Harvey, however, was entirely unmoved in his opinion by such abuse. Only a cannon could shock him out of his scholarly position.

And once a cannon did so. It was at a time when the English king, Charles I, was at war with his Scotch subjects. Harvey was personally attending King Charles, and was present with him at the battle of Edgehill on October 23, 1642.

On that occasion, the king, in a moment of calmness which preceded the battle, noticed that his physician was not to be found. Actually, Harvey was behind a bush at the edge of the hill, deeply immersed in a book he had brought along with him. He was not permitted to read long, for the hostilities would not wait, and a bullet from a gun, grazing the foliage near by, forced him regretfully to change his position.

It turned out that he was no mere spectator of the fight. His book pocketed, he gave as good an account of himself as any. In his treatment of the wounded, he then and there proved the correctness of his theory, which gave him a truer understanding of physiology.

One of the soldiers, Adrian Scrope, having received several wounds, was stripped and left among the dead. His son, who recovered the body, doubtless for burial, encountered Harvey. He, to the amazement of all, brought the man back to life and health. In fact, Adrian Scrope lived to be wounded many more times.

An incident like this inclined people to reflect, "How much Harvey knows about physiology! Maybe the blood does circulate after all."

III

"Maybe!" Such was the doubt the graybeards then cast upon William Harvey.

Today, thanks to scientific discoveries and inventions since Harvey's day, what Harvey had to imagine with deep insight, every medical freshman now can see with his own eyes.

When you have sent for the doctor, the first question he asks is, "How is your circulation?" He does not ask the question with words; he takes your pulse, and waits for the answer to be ticked out to him. He may also listen at your chest for an answer.

"Lubb-dup — lubb-dup," he hears.

The doctor understands. The *lubb-dup* is like the turning of a key to a room wherein he may view the working of your bodily machine. The doctor first takes notice of the pump, your heart. He sees a bag with several chambers through which your stream of life is being sucked in and forced out.

The right side is the entrance for the blood. Purple

in color, it flows in, bereft of its strength and carrying waste. The entranceway is through a flaplike valve which opens and shuts about seventy times a minute. That is your pulse rate if you are not sick. Everywhere there are valves, directing a one-way traffic.

"My heart is beating," you say. What you mean is that your valves are tapping and so making your heart knock against your chest.

When the purple blood is halfway through the heart, it does not go straight on. Surrounding the heart is a spongy organ made up of millions of tiny sacs filled with air — your lungs. In between these sacs the blood spreads and trickles, greedily refreshing itself with the oxygen of the air which the lungs have taken in and which turns it rosy. Then, giving up its own waste, which is carbon dioxide, it returns to the heart, ready to carry the fresh nourishment, the oxygen, through the body.

Out into the main artery it flows — one branch to the head and arms, the other through the trunk and legs. All along the way it leaves its helpful oxygen and carries off the waste. It visits every organ. At the intestines it picks up the absorbed food, takes some of that to the liver, and stores the rest under muscles, around other organs, and under the skin. It does a few other important errands, and by this time is purple for lack of oxygen. But no matter; it is on its way back to the heart again.

Your doctor finds that your heart is knocking against your chest oftener than it should.

"You have a rapid pulse," he says. That may mean that some part of you is in trouble, and the heart has to send it more oxygen than usual. It drives billions of red corpuscles through the blood, therefore, to yield the troubled part as much oxygen as it needs. So the doctor has his clue.

IV

It is curious that although William Harvey was so unworldly that his brother had to take charge of his money in order to prevent him from giving it all away, he was yet hard-headed and sensible.

For instance, in 1634, Edward Robinson, a boy of ten, living in Lancashire, played truant from school. To avoid being punished, he gave as an excuse that he was the victim of a hair-raising adventure. He said that, as he was passing through a thickly-wooded glade, he saw two greyhounds. A hare appeared at the same time, so he tried to incite the dogs, but neither of them would stir. Angry at the beasts, he took up a switch and was about to punish them, when one of the dogs became transformed into a woman, the other into a little boy. In the woman he recognized a neighbor, a certain Mother Dickenson. She offered him money to sell his soul to the devil, but he refused. A host of other witches soon appeared, and Edward Robinson, carried away by his tale, said he could recognize them if he saw them again.

He was led from church to church to identify these evil spirits, and many good persons were arrested on the popular superstition that witches existed. The case became notorious. Seven of those arrested were condemned, when it occurred to the king to ask the advice of William Harvey. Harvey looked into the affair briefly.

"Witches!" he sniffed contemptuously. "Why cannot people be sensible?"

As a result of his report, four of the seven convicted witches were pardoned. Harvey abhorred ignorance and superstition as most people dislike the dark.

He set himself apart, even when past the prime of life, to better his knowledge. He studied mathematics and the anatomy of birds, frogs and toads with the thoroughness which befitted one who in his youth had studied in Italy, then the center of learning. He had graduated at Padua. Upon his diploma, his teachers wrote, "He has surpassed even the great hopes his examiners held for him."

He wrote a good deal at this time, but except for his famous work, *Treatise on the Circulation,* very little has come down to us. "Whilst in attendance on His Majesty the King," Harvey tells, "during our late troubles . . . certain rapacious hands not only stripped my house of all its furniture, but, what is a subject of far greater regret to me, my enemies abstracted from my museum the fruits of many years of toil. Whence it has come to pass that many observations, particularly on the generation of insects, have perished."

"Let gentle minds forgive me," he continues, "if recalling the irreparable injuries I have suffered, I here give vent to a sigh." Contemplative and gentle, with charm and generosity, no wonder this great man was loved far and wide. Amidst the genuine grief of all he went to his grave at the age of seventy, in the summer of 1657.

His discovery of the function of the heart and of the circulation of the blood was the greatest event in medical history up to that time, for it made possible the science of physiology.

Anton van Leeuwenhoek

(1632–1723)

DISCOVERER OF THE
INVISIBLE WORLD

I

IF you had asked an inhabitant of Delft, Holland, what sort of man was Anton van Leeuwenhoek, you would have been told he was queer; a strange, odd man.

"Why?" you might have continued.

"Well, he is a draper by occupation. But his strangeness is not due to that. It is what he is constantly doing in his spare time. First of all he grinds lenses in an odd way. His famous glasses make a thing look two hundred and seventy times bigger than it really is. He has many of them. He will not sell them, nor will he give them away. He guards them jealously and asks you to be careful when he lets you look through them."

"There is nothing funny in that," you say.

"Ah, no. But this is funny: all day long — his duties as draper are light — he goes around with his microscope. He examines everything. If you come to visit him, he may greet you with: 'Hold still for a minute. I'd like to look into your ear . . . Let me peer between your teeth.' He peers at everything — the skin of his hand, the head of a fly, ant eggs."

"Well, does he find anything when he peers?"

"That is the amazing thing. He finds there are many more inhabitants in the world than we can see or dream of. Only yesterday he told me I had a nice garden growing between my teeth. I thought, of course, he was joking, until he scraped my teeth and put the scraping under his glass and, Heaven help me, I saw things move about, living things! And in my barrel of drinking water he found a whole colony of animals alive, which appeared under his glass. To think I have been drinking from that barrel all these years! Where do these animals come from? How? . . . Yes, Leeuwenhoek himself is queer enough, but the things he shows us are queerer still."

It was all true. Other noble souls might discover awe-inspiring planets wending their majestic way in the heavens, but this fellow was inspired by fleas, lice, worms, and creatures ten thousand times smaller, which he tried with his lenses to make look as big as elephants.

No microscope was powerful enough for him. He was constantly making better ones. And the number he made was enormous! Two hundred forty-seven complete microscopes, not counting one hundred seventy-two magnifying lenses.

"Why not?" he defended proudly. "If Aristotle had had my glasses, he would not have made the blunders he did." For Aristotle had said that plant lice arise from dew, and fleas spring from mud. He called this spontaneous generation.

This was a common belief, and a learned man of that day had even given out a recipe for making mice. "Put some dirty linen in a basket," he wrote, "together with a few grains of wheat and a piece of cheese. In a few days, a mouse, two, three, and many more, will come of it all."

"This is not true," maintained Leeuwenhoek. "I have seen creatures hatched from minute eggs brought by winged insects or by the dust of the air. Every living thing, no matter how small, has a parent. Spontaneous generation is a fable; nothing else. Not only are fleas born in the usual way, but sometimes they are attacked and fed upon by a mite — in other words, even a flea may have its own fleas to worry it."

> . . . a flea
> *Has smaller fleas that on him prey;*
> *And these have smaller still to bite 'em;*
> *And so proceed ad infinitum.*

II

With his magic lenses Leeuwenhoek discovered the world of one-celled beings, more astounding than any dream world, more important than Columbus'; billions upon billions of living animals and plants around us, upon us, within us.

He looked at rain water. What could he hope to discover there? Yet soon fantastic shapes could be made out. Excitedly he watched these animalcules, creatures unlike those we see with the naked eye, swimming in water. Like Columbus, he had discovered a world — the world of first life — Protozoa.

"I've discovered," he wrote elatedly to the Royal Society in England, "living creatures in rain water which

had stood but a few days in a new earthen pot . . .
Those little animals appeared to me ten thousand
times smaller than water fleas, which may be perceived
in the water with the naked eye . . . When they
moved, they put forth two little horns. The place between these two horns was flat, though the rest of the
body was roundish, sharpening a little towards the end,
where they had a tail, near four times the length of the
whole body, of the thickness of a spider web . . ."

Here is another kind, "moving about very nimbly,
furnished with incredibly thin feet." Sometimes "they
stop, they stand still as 'twere upon a point, and then
turn themselves round with that swiftness, as we see a
top turn round, the circumference they make being no
bigger than that of a fine grain of sand."

The Society was utterly bewildered. Their imagination had roamed in the realms of immense things: fab-
ulous unicorns the size of elephants, and fiery hippo-
griffs, and birds like Sindbad's roc whose egg was as
large as a hill. But here was a real animal whose whole
body was nothing but one single, solitary cell. And that
is next to nothing at all. Why, the tip of the finger has
thousands of cells!

The more they thought about it, the more amazing it
seemed. How could any one imagine an animal — living, breathing, moving from place to place, eating,
preying greedily on other animals — and itself the size
of one cell! Why, a flea must appear to be a whole
world to it.

A teacup, filled with dirty water, must have a greater
population than the human population of America.

The world would have liked to doubt all this. It was

so uncomfortable to feel that upon you, inside you, on your food, you were entertaining parties of unbidden guests. It was more uncomfortable to feel that you could do nothing about it. But how could anyone doubt?

"Take a little water from a rain spout and look at it through a microscope," he insisted.

Through the microscope people were able to observe protozoa and the struggle for life among them. Their one cell is made of something like jelly. Yet they are not alike, Leeuwenhoek saw. They differ as much as a dog and an elephant.

"But what is their shape? And how can they eat, and breathe, and get about — all with one cell?"

That *is* strange. But just watch the microscope! One of the most ordinary of Protozoa is called the amoeba. He cannot be said to have any sort of shape, he changes so. Now watch him. This living speck of jelly somehow flows and rolls along, in search of dinner. It happens that another but smaller one-celled being crosses the path of our hero, the amoeba. A tense moment!

Suddenly the amoeba, resorting to strategy, surrounds his enemy. That is the advantage of being shapeless.

Poor captive protozoan! No quarter is shown him. He finds himself surprisingly inside the amoeba. Any convenient part of the amoeba, you see, is his mouth, and on the inside he is all stomach. When he grows too big, he divides in half, and there are two amoebae, where once there was but one.

Some protozoa prefer the sea. When that is the case, as creatures of the deep they are usually fitted with shells, just like the more masterful snail or turtle. If in life one-celled things seem insignificant, in death the sea protozoa serve nobly. As they die, the shells sink, pile up, turn to rock, and in aeons of time the pile rises up out of the sea . . . Protozoa built the famous chalk cliffs of England.

Leeuwenhoek was puzzled by one matter. Whence came the amoebae in the rain water? "Surely, not from the sky," he thought. To find out, he took a big porcelain dish and, washing it clean, he carried it out into the rain and put it on top of a big box. "No mud must splash into the dish," he thought, "for mud contains living beings." He studied the rain water. It did not contain a single creature. Therefore, they do not come from the sky.

But he kept that water. Hour after hour, day after day, he peered at it. Then one day, he saw animalcules begin to appear along with bits of dust.

But he was cautious. He turned his glass on all conditions of water, water from wells and from the canals of Delft. In all gutters he found the wee beasts. "The dust carries them there," he said.

"Every living thing," he repeated, "has a parent."

III

One day the Royal Society received another letter from Leeuwenhoek. "Although I am now fifty years old," they read, "I have well-preserved teeth, because it is my custom every morning to rub my teeth very hard with salt, and after cleaning my large teeth with a quill, to rub them vigorously with a cloth . . . Nevertheless, when I view them with a magnifying glass, I find growing between them a little white matter as thick as wetted flour. I thought that in this substance lurked living creatures.

"I therefore took some of this flour and mixed it with pure rain water wherein were no animals; and to my great surprise saw many small living creatures moving about. The biggest sort darted through the water, as a pike-fish does. Some spun like a top. Others looked like bent sticks or threads . . . but some were small and swift, like a swarm of flies or gnats, flying and turning among one another in a small space. Of this sort, I believe there might be many thousands in a quantity of water no bigger than a grain of sand." As living things, he saw a vast difference between these creatures and those he had formerly seen in the standing rain water. Before he had discovered Protozoa; now he discovered bacteria, the one-celled plants.

He began to examine everybody he could enlist. He studied two women, a child of eight years, the spittle of an old man. He gazed upon a great many tiny living creatures, swimming more nimbly than any he had ever seen.

As the years went by, he continued his careful observations. All Europe began now to recognize him. When Peter the Great of Russia visited Holland, he came to pay his respects to Leeuwenhoek. The Dutchman let the Czar peer through his magnifying lens to examine the circulation of blood in the tail of an eel. The Queen of England journeyed especially to Delft to look at the wonders to be seen through his lenses. Success, however, did not spoil him. He worked all the harder for it.

"Captain," he begged a fisherman, "promise you will some day bring me the eye of a whale."

"Hans," he would instruct his servant, "this afternoon you will catch me a few fleas. But take care not to hold them too tightly. You may hurt them."

The world was so full of wonderful things! He could think of no greater joy than to put a piece of the bark of a tree under his lens — and then what a strange thing he saw! No longer was it a mere splinter of brown wood. It became a marvelous network of fibers, never before so seen. And if he were lucky, he might find hidden in the bark the minute eggs of some insect.

Leeuwenhoek continued to write lengthy letters to the Royal Society. Generally they were in Dutch, though occasionally someone would translate his letter into Latin. He described the muscle fibers of a whale, of a codfish, and of a duck's heart. He wrote down his observations on human blood corpuscles, on the liver of a pig, the bladder of an ox. Under the lens of his microscope he put the hair of a sheep, a beaver's, an elk's, and a bear's; also the scales of a perch, the web of a spider as well as its spinning apparatus. Also the eyes of a spider and of a dragonfly.

With all his peering he never realized what his discoveries were later to mean. It was left for Louis Pasteur, two hundred years later, to show that bacteria cause fevers, lockjaw, tuberculosis, diphtheria. With these enemy bacteria our heroes of medicine do battle. Not that all bacteria are enemies of mankind. Our agriculture could not go on but for friendly bacteria; nor could we make cheese or buttermilk. And our digestion, when it is good, depends on the helpful sort of bacteria.

Yet it is true — and Leeuwenhoek would have been astounded to know it — that his Protozoa toppled Rome from her greatness. For ages it was known that people living in the swampy places near Rome were subject to attacks of malaria. In Rome itself thousands fell victim to the fever. To get rid of this dread disease seemed beyond the hopes of man. "What causes malaria?" people asked. "Bad air," the doctors ventured. But not until long after was it realized that malaria is caused by a kind of protozoan that lives on the blood of man.

When Leeuwenhoek learned about William Harvey and his great discovery of blood circulation, he turned his lens on the bloodstream. Harvey had never been able to see the blood flowing through the capillaries or its pouring from the arteries to the veins. He just reasoned it out. But Leeuwenhoek was unsatisfied till he had seen it.

To bring before his eyes the blood circulation, he experimented with all kinds and parts of animals; the comb of a young cock, the tail of an eel, the ears of white rabbits, the wings of a bat, the web of a frog's foot. One day he examined the transparent tail of a tadpole. Here was a sight more delightful than any he had ever beheld. For his eyes traced the red corpuscles floating through wide arteries, which taper so narrowly that the corpuscles must squeeze their way through the capillaries into the veins.

When he was ninety-one years old, Leeuwenhoek sent for his friend Hoogvliet. "Hoogvliet, my friend," he said, "be so good as to have those two letters on the table translated into Latin. Send them to London to the Royal Society . . ."

"I send you, learned sirs," Hoogvliet wrote, "this last gift of my dying friend, hoping that his final word will be agreeable to you."

Agreeable! Leeuwenhoek had brought to light a startling world of animals and plants whose lives are intertwined with those of the human race.

Edward Jenner

(1749–1823)

A MODERN THESEUS

I

AT ABOUT the time of the American Revolution, a group of distinguished Englishmen were enjoying the holiday season at Bath. They met one evening to dine and make merry, when a discussion arose.

"You are wrong," said one. "The hottest part of a candle flame is the center."

"Oh, no," said another. "It seems to me that the hottest part is near the apex.

So it went, back and forth, without reaching any conclusion, when suddenly a young man stepped forward and seized a lighted candle.

"Gentlemen," he said, "be silent and look." He placed the candle before him, and before anyone could stop him, he had thrust his finger into the center of the flame.

"It's a trifle warm," he smiled, "but you see it . . ." At this point he was compelled to withdraw his finger.

"Now for the apex." He advanced his finger cautiously, but no sooner had he touched the bluish part of the flame than he exclaimed in pain and withdrew his finger.

The question was settled.

"Who is that young man?" whispered a certain diplomat to Dr. Beddoes, who was later to be the employer of Humphry Davy.

"That is Dr. Edward Jenner."

"What an able scientist!" said the diplomat fervidly. "I am so impressed with him that I shall obtain for him a post of high authority in the East Indies. The nation ought to recognize its men of talent."

Beddoes shook his head. "No use trying that," he returned. "You can no more get him out of his small country town, where he studies the birds and flowers and tends the sick, than you can induce a fish to leave the water."

A clapping of hands interrupted this conversation. They turned and saw Jenner standing in the middle of the room with a paper in his hand. "They have prevailed on him to read his poetry," said Beddoes. "I think he is one of the best of poets. Listen."

"This is on the death of a miser," began Jenner slowly. "It isn't very good . . ."

"Never mind what you think," said one of the number. "Let us judge."

"Well then:

> Tom at last has laid by his old niggardly forms,
> And now gives good dinners; to whom, pray? —
> the worms."

Shouts and laughter rang out, "Bravo! More! More!"

"If you like," said the shy poet . . .

II

The Minotaur was a fabled monster of ancient times who demanded the yearly sacrifice of seven youths and seven maidens. The hero Thesus finally slew him. In modern times a specter far more terrible than the Minotaur afflicted mankind. Invisibly it stalked the earth and took its toll of men, women and children. Its name was smallpox, and by the time the eighteenth century was coming to a close no Theseus had yet arisen.

Upon every mother lay the pall of constant fear. Any day her child or her husband might be seized by the dread disease, the victim stupefied by fever and chills, his body breaking out in pustules. If he recovered — the chance was slim — he carried to the end of his days the mark of the specter: disfigurement, lameness or blindness.

Men prayed that the disease might come to them early in life. They knew that for some reason the disease struck a person once only, and everyone wished to be free of the daily anxiety on its account.

Where did the specter come from? No one knew. It was everywhere. It swept through Rome about twenty-five hundred years ago leaving so many dead that there were not enough wagons to carry them away. From earliest times it was known in Egypt, in India, in China. In Ceylon it wiped out entire villages. In Russia it had been known to cut down two million people in a single year. Every seventh child became its victim. Throughout the world during a twenty-five-year period one and a half million people died of smallpox. Three out of every four who recovered were blinded.

Edward Jenner, a twenty-six-year-old doctor in Gloucestershire, England, was examining his patient, a young milkmaid.

"You'll be fit again in a few days," he said. "It isn't smallpox, if that's what you feared."

"Oh no, sir. I was not afraid of that. I cannot get the smallpox. You see, I've already had the cowpox."

Dr. Jenner was intrigued. Was there really a connection between smallpox and cowpox? The question was sufficiently important to be looked into. He went to all the nearby villages. Every farmhand confirmed what the milkmaid said. It seemed to be a well-attested fact that anyone who was lucky enough to have caught cowpox, not at all serious to humans, was safe from smallpox. Jenner could not doubt that there was a connection between the two diseases. He conjectured that they must be one and the same, that the disease took one form in cattle and another in human beings. In a short while a chain of events made him certain of this.

On a farm one day his attention was drawn to a horse which had become infected by a hoof disease known as "grease." By itself this was not an important case. But in a few days the pox broke out among cows and swine. Dr. Jenner was interested. "Grease," then cowpox and swinepox. What would happen next? For one thing, a milkmaid was made happy by discovering that her hands were covered with cowpox. Now what? Jenner waited, expectant, torn between hope and fear. If there was indeed a connection between "grease," cowpox and smallpox, then he feared for the villagers. His fears were tragically realized: an epidemic of smallpox broke out.

As a doctor there wasn't much he could do for the victims. But as he went among them doing what he could to alleviate their agony there was born in him a great hope. He was reasonably sure of the connection between smallpox and cowpox. He would of course have to test his theory. If it turned out to be true, then smallpox could perhaps be prevented. That was the hope.

To test his theory he needed a volunteer. Whom could he ask? He himself was immune to smallpox. He couldn't ask anyone else to risk his life. He spoke to his wife, the mother of his son. They considered the yearly tribute that mankind was forced to pay the Minotaur. Someone had to challenge it. Dr. Jenner did not deny the risk. As a father he would shield his son's life with his own. But thinking of others, of a whole world of people now and to come, he felt that his personal happiness was of small account. What troubled days and nights father and mother had! In the end they came to the belief that it was not right to ask others to make a sacrifice that they themselves were unwilling to make.

"Anyhow," said Dr. Jenner to his wife, "I am confident that the risk isn't great."

"Let us pray that you are right, Edward."

Little Edward's arm was bared and matter from the swinepox pustules injected into it. The injection brought about the expected mild form of the disease. The boy suffered hardly at all.

Now came the great ordeal for father and mother,

and for the scientist Dr. Jenner the crucial point of the experiment. The only cheerful one of the three was little Edward. Secure in his father's love, he held up his arm as his father told him to do. Into his son's arm Dr. Jenner injected pus from the sores of a victim of smallpox.

Days and nights of unbearable anxiety! Dr. Jenner kept watching his son for symptoms. The days passed and little Edward stayed chipper as always. At last the load of anxiety was lifted from the parents and Dr. Jenner, the scientist, felt that the experiment had succeeded. The vaccine, as he called it, had conferred immunity from smallpox.

Before he could make the announcement to other doctors, however, he had to settle certain questions. Either cowpox vaccine or swinepox vaccine would give protection against smallpox. But which was the better? How much vaccine made up a dose? When was the best time to administer it? It took seven years for Dr. Jenner to work out the answers. Then, in 1796, on May 14 — in Berlin they used to call it Jenner's day and make it a holiday — he vaccinated James Phipps, a healthy boy eight years of age. Following the vaccination he inoculated the child with the pus of smallpox. Dr. Jenner was sure of the result and he prepared to make the announcement: Let the world rejoice. James Phipps was immune to the dread disease of smallpox.

Theseus had slain the Minotaur. Fable had become fact.

III

The name Jenner became a household word. In Russia the first child to be vaccinated was christened Vaccinove and pensioned for life by the Czar, who also sent gifts to the English country doctor. From the other side of the world American Indians expressed their gratitude by sending Dr. Jenner a wampum (money) belt. President Jefferson wrote to the doctor: "You have erased from the calendar of human affliction one of its greatest. Mankind can never forget that you have lived."

In London a Jenner Society was founded which urged him to transfer his practice to the city. "We guarantee you £10,000 yearly," they wrote. But he preferred to remain where he was, in his country house where he studied nature and tended the poor and sick. For vaccinating his people he refused to take money. On some days more than three hundred people gathered outside his door, each one waiting his turn to be vaccinated.

One day in the palace of Napoleon Bonaparte the Empress Josephine was reading aloud a petition lately arrived from England. Napoleon was pacing the floor.

"No, no," he interrupted. "What! Release the English prisoners! Never."

Josephine kept on reading, Napoleon shaking his head. When she finished Napoleon stopped. He had caught the sound of a name.

"Who? Who signed the petition?"

"Edward Jenner."

"Ah," sighed Napoleon. "We can refuse nothing to that man."

Louis Pasteur

(1822–1895)

"LOOK FOR THE GERM . . ."

I

THE brewers of Paris were alarmed; hundreds of casks of beer were spoiling. The vintners of France were likewise alarmed; hundreds of vats of wine had turned to vinegar. They appealed for help to a young professor of chemistry, Louis Pasteur.

Professor Pasteur put a specimen of the bitter beer under the microscope. He did the same with the sour wine. The liquids were alive with creatures, microscopic models of industry. He showed them to the brewers and vintners. "These are the rascals that are ruining your product," he said. "Rid your vats and your casks of these germs and your industry will be saved."

The brewers and the vintners were inclined to be skeptical. How could these creatures, so small as to be invisible to the naked eye, get into a vat? Leeuwenhoek had proved that there was one way at least, through the air. And it was discovered that you could rid the air of microbes by sterilization. Pasteur demonstrated this to his doubting clients. He sterilized the air in a room. Then he heated a sample of beer. The liquid kept good and sweet.

Today, before milk is bottled, we do the same. We heat the milk to a high enough temperature to kill any germs that may have found their way into the liquid. We call this "pasteurization." Many communities permit only pasteurized milk to be sold, for in no other way can people be protected against diseases which may be spread by infected milk.

Pasteur explained that the dust in the air is laden with germs and microbes. The dust falling into the liquid deposits the bacteria, and they multiply fast. "Keep your vats free of dust," he advised the brewers.

As he said this a remarkable idea occurred to him. In the name of the thousands upon thousands of people whose lives have been prolonged by it, the world will never forget it. What flashed into Pasteur's mind was this:

"If microbes or germs cause beverages to go bad and food to rot, would they not also be the cause of disease in the human body?"

"Look for the germ," he advised physicians. "Destroy it before it destroys your patient."

II

Who was Louis Pasteur?

An old letter dated February 10, 1849, tells us. He wrote the letter when he fell in love with Marie Laurent of Strasbourg. The love was mutual, but as a gentleman Pasteur was required to appeal for Marie's hand to her father. Pasteur was then twenty-six years old, and Professor of Chemistry at the University of

Strasbourg. That much Monsieur Laurent knew already, but the suitor felt obliged to tell everything about himself.

"My father," he wrote, "is a tanner in the small town of Arbois in the Jura. My sisters are with him and take care of the household and help in the trade. We had the great misfortune to lose our mother last May.

"My family is quite comfortable, but by no means wealthy. I would not value our possessions at more than 50,000 francs, and I have long ago decided to hand over my share in full to my sisters. Therefore I have no property at all. My only assets are good health, an honest heart and my position at the University.

"I graduated from the École Normale two years ago. I have held a doctor's degree for the past eighteen months, and some studies of mine which I presented to the Academy of Sciences have been well received.

"This, sir, is my present situation. As to my future, I am determined to devote myself to chemical research. It is my ambition to return to Paris when I have acquired some reputation."

Three months later Marie and Louis were married.

When he announced his germ theory of infectious disease, Louis Pasteur was in Paris, professor at the École Normale.

Most doctors were skeptical of his germ theory. "Just because Pasteur has made a discovery in the field of chemistry — something about crystals — he has grown a bit cocky," they grumbled. "Let him stick to chemistry and not trespass into medicine."

Pasteur's opportunity came to prove his germ theory.

From Cévennes and neighboring districts in the south of France came a cry of distress. The people were being robbed of their living by a mysterious disease which was destroying the silkworm, sole source of their livelihood. Similarly afflicted were districts in Italy, in Spain, in Greece, in Turkey, in China and wherever the silkworm was grown. In the south of France workers in the silk industry were slowly starving. They appealed to Paris, and in turn the government appealed to Louis Pasteur.

"But I have never even seen a silkworm," he said.

It was a time of bitter sorrow for himself. In June of that year, 1865, his father died; in September his little son Camille; the following spring his daughter Cécile. From grief and overwork he himself sickened and almost died. Nevertheless, he traveled to the stricken districts in the south. He tracked down the germ that ruined the silk crop and he taught the silkworm growers how to destroy the germ. The people of the Cévennes mountains could have worshiped him, for he had saved them from starvation.

Another opportunity came to test the theory. In the poultry farms of France there broke out an epidemic of chicken cholera. In every barnyard every sunrise told its mournful tale. Here a hen brooding on her nest, dead; there a superb cock which only yesterday had crowed so lustily, now rigid in the dust.

The food loss to the French people was alarming. Again the help of Pasteur was sought and he went to work on the problem. Under his microscope the blood of the diseased fowl showed up the tiny killers. Pasteur knew that a drop of this blood injected into a healthy fowl would cause cholera. A new idea occurred to him, or rather he remembered an old one. He remembered that Edward Jenner had made people immune to smallpox by vaccinating them with a mild form of the disease itself. Would a mild form of cholera make fowl immune to the disease?

He put some cholera blood into a dish of broth. "Let this culture stand awhile," he told his assistants.

He let several weeks go by. When he judged that the germs were considerably weakened he inoculated a flock of fowl with the culture. After a sleepless night he went to his laboratory, and to his delight he found the fowls lively. Now for the crucial test.

His assistants brought him a fresh batch of cholera culture and a flock of new chickens. He inoculated both the new and the old flock with the deadly cholera germs. The result of the experiment: only the new flock died. The old flock was as lively as ever. They had become immune. Louis Pasteur now announced his formula for the treatment of disease. "Find the germ," he advised. "Then turn it into vaccine for the patient."

Doctors were still not convinced.

Among the cattle of France the dread disease called anthrax broke out. Half the livestock of France were dying. A sheep would be seen lagging behind the rest of the flock, his limbs shaking. A spurt of thick blood would gush out of its mouth, its body becoming convulsed. A few hours later anthrax had claimed another victim.

Pasteur's opponents, those who had ridiculed his idea of vaccines, now challenged him to make a vaccine against anthrax. They offered fifty sheep for the trial.

Pasteur accepted the challenge and on a farm near the city of Chartres in the spring of 1881 the experiment was tried. To witness the event came doctors, journalists and scientists from everywhere.

Pasteur divided the fifty sheep into two groups of twenty-five each. One group he inoculated with a vaccine he had made against anthrax. The other group was not so treated. Then the deadly anthrax microbes were injected into all fifty sheep. Result of the experiment: the twenty-five vaccinated sheep kept browsing in the fields in good health; the others died.

There was no longer any doubt. From that day on Louis Pasteur had no opponents. The world, in fact, was awed by his genius, and a chorus of gratitude went up for the man who had discovered a way of reducing the sum of human misery. He himself remained as humble and hardworking as before. He once accepted an invitation to attend an international medical congress in London. When he arrived in the hall he was recognized by a steward and bidden to mount the platform. As he walked down the aisle a thunderous applause burst from the assembly.

"I suppose the Prince of Wales is arriving," said Pasteur to the chairman as he mounted the platform.

The chairman held out his hand. "No, it is you," he said. "It is you whom they are cheering."

There was a time when nothing was feared so much as the bite of a mad dog. The victim with his intense desire for water, his choking spasms and his excruciating suffering just before he died so terrified everyone around that he was usually abandoned and left to die alone. Many fantastic tales were told of those bitten by a mad dog. "They bark like dogs," it was said. "They go on all fours."

The cures suggested were even stranger. In olden times, for instance, a famous doctor wrote: "The only remedy is to throw the patient unexpectedly into a pond. If he cannot swim let him sink in order that he may drink the water: and when he rises again push him again below the surface of the water so that even if he is unwilling he will be sated with water. But if the water cure enfeebles the patient too much let him be taken from the water and put in hot oil."

For centuries various remedies were tried. One doctor seriously thought that a wound made by a mad dog should be enlarged, packed with gunpowder, and exploded. If any patient were foolish enough to follow such advice his friends soon found him cured not only of rabies but of all ailments forever.

To Pasteur, rabies, or hydrophobia, was only another germ-caused disease and he made a vaccine which he hoped would cure it. Whether it would or not could only be determined by a grim test. And soon enough came the need to put the vaccine to the test. In a room in Paris lay a boy of nine who had been bitten fourteen times by a mad dog. The boy's mother stood by the bedside wringing her hands. She had brought her son to Paris from a distant province. She had nothing but blind faith in a name. "Pasteur," she implored.

In an adjoining room two doctors were urging Louis Pasteur to act. "Professor," they said, "the boy is as good as dead. There is nothing to be lost by trying your antirabic vaccine."

Pasteur was pacing the room, agitated. "Dare I?" he groaned. "I have never tried it on a human patient. It is effective with animals. Who knows what it might do to a child? If it fails and little Joseph dies I shall feel responsible."

"Still, we doctors can do nothing for the boy."

Pasteur had no choice. If he failed it would break his heart, but he must risk it. The inoculation was administered to Joseph. Now a period of waiting set in. In two weeks' time the tale would be told and the boy either die or recover. During the critical period Pasteur hardly slept or ate. He was in fact on the verge of breaking down when Joseph began definitely to mend. So did Louis Pasteur. Not only did Joseph recover but he grew up and spent his long life in the service of the Pasteur Institute.

To Paris from all over the world came people afflicted with rabies. Four American boys came, sent by charity. After the first inoculation, which took only a few seconds, the youngest boy — he was five — said, "Is this all? Did we come all the way for just this?" How could a boy of five know that the kindly man who bent over them with so sweet a smile had in a few seconds saved his life?

There is no civilized land in the world which has not paid its respect to Louis Pasteur. His name has been given to hospitals, to towns and to streets.

Once, when the school children of France were asked to name the greatest Frenchman, it was expected that they would choose Napoleon, the man of blood and glory. The children knew better. They chose Louis Pasteur.

Robert Koch

(1843–1910)

FATHER OF BACTERIOLOGY

I

"CAN it be?" Dr. Robert Koch wondered. "Can these strange rods and threads really be so deadly?"

His eye was glued fast to the microscope — a pastime at which he had often been found ever since he was seventeen, when his father had presented him with the microscope. But this time he was especially absorbed. He was gazing down on a drop of the blackish blood of a dead cow, recently killed by that terrible curse, anthrax. Louis Pasteur had not yet begun his brilliant campaign against this disease, but the farmers were already crying out that they would be ruined unless this malady was stamped out. It was small consolation to them that the great Pasteur had boldly declared, "Every disease is caused by a germ."

"To begin with, the declaration, without proof to back it up, is ridiculous. Show the germ! Let us look him in the eye! Let us see him at his murdering work of blackening the blood, choking the blood vessels, and eating up the tissues. Otherwise, why waste thought on this tiniest of living things?" That was the people's attitude.

And the slow, painstaking country doctor, Robert Koch, was in sympathy with such an attitude. "This fellow Pasteur, genius though he be, is far too reckless and impulsive. If anthrax, for instance, is caused by a germ, he ought to show us . . ."

It occurred to him that he might find out for himself. Anthrax in his farm district of Wollstein, Germany, was under his very window. He knew the sad truth, that the very cow that had tolled her bell as she passed his study only yesterday, would doubtless be dead now. The mournful farmer would tell how she had suddenly refused to eat; how her head had drooped and her splendid hulk had sagged; how, before he had realized her trouble, she had died. Then, he knew, other cattle in the same field would die, perhaps all of them. What mysterious power was at work?

"If Pasteur is right," reasoned Koch, "then I ought to see microbes in the blood of this dead cow. But are these rods and threads, these microbes, alive?" He saw them floating in the globule of blood, some long and wavy like threads, others short and straight like rods. "Now here's a drop of healthy cow's blood. There are none of these rods and threads in it. Does that prove that these rods and threads are the anthrax germs?"

Not quite; not for the cautious Koch. He must see the microbes at work.

He selected two mice. One he left as it was. In the tail of the other he made a tiny cut. He dipped a sliver of sterilized wood into the drop of diseased black blood and then touched it to the cut. The mice were put in separate cages.

"Now we shall see."

The night was restless for the doctor. Too much depended on this experiment for him to sleep peacefully. In the morning he ran eagerly to visit the mice. One was dead — the one with the cut in its tail. Its blackish blood swarmed with millions of those familiar rods and threads. Under Koch's very eye the microbes multiplied. A rod would divide in two. The two halves would grow. Then they would each divide again, and keep on in this manner until they seemed likely to outdo even the multiplication table.

"How can I study these rods?" he asked. "It's difficult enough because they are so tiny — twenty-five thousand to the inch; but if only they didn't move! I must keep them fixed somehow, if I am to learn anything at all about anthrax."

For days he wore a worried look. The country folk were sure their doctor was wasting his time looking for tiny bugs too small to be seen by the eye — and yet he claimed that these bugs killed the strongest ox. "Our doctor has a vivid imagination," was their comment. But Dr. Koch was too busy even to listen to country gossip. He had to find some way of training the bacteria to remain fixed. But how?

"If I could somehow glue them fast — and yet I must not kill them. To find out how they cause us mischief, I must feed them, nourish them, and let them grow big and strong."

The doctor's eyes suddenly lighted. "Why must the

bacteria roam in a liquid? Can I not make them thrive on solid food? And yet, how could I look at a microbe hidden away under a solid mass? Ah! I know. My microbe food must be transparent, so that I can look through it at the microbe itself. Perhaps if I make the food somewhat solid . . ."

He waited until some neighboring farmer was ready to slaughter an ox. Dr. Koch then set to work. Carefully he steamed a test tube for about an hour and a half. That heating was to kill any kind of bacteria that might be lurking in the tube. Then, when he felt sure that the tube was clean, he plugged the mouth of the tube with cotton wool.

"If my idea works, I shall be able to raise all the bacteria I need, and they will not move from the spot on which I put them. An ideal food — solid, and yet transparent," he muttered to himself as he hurried to the farmer.

"Is there anything you want, Doctor?" the farmer asked respectfully.

"After you kill the animal, permit me to open one of its arteries. I need some fresh blood for my experiments," and he held up his test tube.

He carried the test tube, filled with warm blood, back to his laboratory, holding it all the way carefully, so as not to shake it. For a day he let the blood cool in the glass tube. The clear serum of the blood meanwhile separated itself from the coagulated thick blood. Koch added some gelatin to this serum so that it might become firm.

Now for the test. Would the anthrax bacilli like the new home he planned for them? Slowly he poured a few drops of this liquid on a smooth glass. In it he placed a drop of blood from an animal that had just died of anthrax. The jelly hardened and held the bacteria fixed. Yet the serum was so clear that Robert Koch could watch the germs to his heart's content.

His gaze was soon rewarded. The microbe had divided into two, and these two new bacteria were slowly growing. After a time these divided. "How rapidly they grow!" he marveled. His pencil scrawled some numbers on paper. "Suppose one of these bacilli were to divide into two in twenty minutes, and twenty minutes later, each new microbe reach the size of the original and then again divide, and then again, and so on, dividing every twenty minutes. In eight hours, we should have sixteen million germs! That's why these little rods are so dangerous. One germ can not harm you, but put it in the human blood, where it will thrive, and see what happens!"

Koch's idea was right. In a short time the serum was covered with little specks, each speck consisting of a whole colony of germs.

"I wonder if the bacteria like sunshine," he thought. He put them outside. Strange! He found that a ray of sunlight was like a glimmer of death to them.

II

A perplexing thought came to him. "If these bacteria are so delicate, how is it they can live in the fields, lurking in the grass and weeds of the open air?"

The question continued to plague him until one day an amazing sight gave him the answer. As he was paying his morning compliments to the microbe colony, a re-markable change came over it. All the rods and threads became little beadlike drops. Dumbfounded, Koch put these shining beadlike forms into fresh liquid, properly heated. Back again to rods and threads they turned.

"So that's it!" cried Koch. "These beads are the spores, the tough form of the microbe, the form it takes in the fields. In this guise it can withstand the dry and cold weather. When the cattle graze in the fields, they swallow the spores, which in the blood become those fatal rods and threads."

He felt confident that he was not mistaken. Writing to Professor Cohn, of the University of Breslau, a fa-mous botanist, Koch asked the privilege of seeing him. "I have made a great discovery," he wrote.

Now Professor Cohn had received many letters from unknown men claiming that they had made great dis-coveries, but when he examined their claims, he usu-ally found them false. Therefore he did not look for-ward to the visit of this country doctor.

It did not take Professor Cohn long to find out that Robert Koch could prove everything he asserted. Hur-riedly he sent a messenger to the Pathological Institute, asking that someone come to his laboratory because a visitor, a Dr. Koch, had something to show which was "very interesting."

In the Pathological Institute, there was a great scien-tist, Professor Cohnheim. He went across to the Botani-cal Laboratory, where Koch was displaying his germs.

Back rushed the professor to the Institute. "Stop everything here, and go over to Koch," he shouted to his assistants. "The man has made a tremendous discovery!"

Koch's remarkable discovery, as he told them, was this: only an anthrax germ can cause anthrax; only a typhoid germ can cause typhoid. Every disease has its particular germ; and every germ is responsible for a special disease.

"But tell us how to stamp out this curse of anthrax," the farmers cried.

"Destroy the bodies of all animals killed by anthrax. Kill the bacilli," answered Koch.

III

The genius of the man who made so remarkable a discovery was recognized. He was made a professor of medicine and a member of the Imperial Board of Health of Berlin; he was given a fine laboratory there, and money and assistants to carry on his fight against all diseases. One by one he attacked each special germ. With the help of his assistants, he found and photographed the germs of eleven important human diseases, among which are tuberculosis, cholera, typhoid, diphtheria, pneumonia, and the bubonic plague.

He was to be found in almost any part of the world, exposing and destroying germs. Everywhere mankind was to be served. He went to Egypt and India to root out cholera and, thanks to him, that disease is now rarely active in Europe and America. On the island of Brien, in the Adriatic, he vanquished malaria. Even when he was past sixty he traveled to a desolate island in Lake Victoria Nyanza to study the blood-sucking tsetse fly, which carries the germ of sleeping sickness. On this island he lived in a rough cabin, with only one companion, and their only means of reaching the mainland was a rough canoe, hewn out of a log.

An idea of what mankind owes to Robert Koch may be gained from a few facts:

From earliest days, epidemics of bubonic plague wrought havoc over the face of the earth. During the fourteenth century alone this Black Death, raging in Asia and Europe, destroyed one-fourth of the population of the world.

Koch tracked down its germ.

Cholera had existed for hundreds of years in India, and at times had appeared elsewhere.

Koch, as head of a German commission sent to Egypt and India to investigate cholera, discovered the cholera bacterium.

His greatest triumph, however, was over tuberculosis, that disease under which so much human life had wasted away through long centuries. During the nineteenth century, over thirty million people died from it. From time immemorial every third or fourth adult, between his youth and fifty-fifth birthday, succumbed to the Great White Plague.

"Tuberculosis is inherited," the doctors gloomily said. "If your father had it, you will have it. What can man do? Can he flee from his inheritance?"

But Dr. Koch was hopeful: "We are just beginning to understand diseases. Perhaps some germ is the mischief maker." He therefore looked at the blood of one of the tubercular victims. There he found tiny bacteria rods.

"These cause tuberculosis," he thought. "In a healthy man's blood I find no bacteria like these." However, he did not feel ready to announce his discovery, for he was thorough in all he did. To make sure, thought he, one must first be able to grow a microbe colony, and then he must see if these microbes really cause tuberculosis. Strangely, the germs died in the serum he prepared for them.

Robert Koch was perplexed. "I must try another kind of broth." But all attempts to grow the germs failed.

"That's strange. Why don't these bacteria like my broth?"

Then the picture of millions suffering, with their consumptive coughs and their expectation of death, determined him. "I must find a way to keep these bacilli alive. I must study the germ — to relieve mankind of such desolation. Since this broth doesn't suit them, I must experiment until I find some serum they will like and thrive on." The result of Doctor Koch's long and patient search was a special mixture of blood serum and glycerin. Now he could keep the bacteria alive. At least, so it seemed.

Ten days he waited anxiously before he could see the rods grow.

To Robert Koch the next step was all important. "Perhaps these germs do not cause tuberculosis after all. My eyes must see." Therefore he injected a speck of the germ colony, which he had raised, into some healthy mice. Soon their blood was swarming with tiny rods.

"These bacilli cause tuberculosis," he could now announce to the world. Robert Koch had found the germ. And with his great discovery as a guide, doctors could lay plans to defeat the Great White Plague, even to prevent its start. Thanks to Koch, the death rate from tuberculosis has fallen considerably.

He was, however, very modest in spite of his deserved fame. Like a true scientist, he said of his experiments, "They should be repeated by others to prove that I am right."

The Nobel Prize for medicine was given him in 1905, and the rulers of almost every European State showered honors upon him. When he died at Baden-Baden in 1910, the English journal, *Nature,* wrote: "The death of Robert Koch is a loss not only to Germany; all mankind is the poorer."

Joseph Lister

(1827–1912)

SURGERY MADE SAFE

I

IN PARIS Louis Pasteur was still breathless with the vision of a new world. He was looking at tiny beasts toiling to change sugar to alcohol, to make milk turn sour and beer become bad.

At this time a young English doctor, Joseph Lister, was on his way to Glasgow to serve in the hospital there. As he journeyed, he pictured a wounded man brought to him, the poor fellow's face ashen, his eye glassy, and his mouth taut with agony . . . And then he drew a picture that flushed his grave brow, he saw himself examine the wound, heal it, and send the grateful man, saved from death, back to the bosom of his family with steady gaze and firm step.

Vain dream! Lister had no sooner begun his duties than it vanished. In the wards of the Glasgow Hospital he looked upon wounded limbs, stretched out, bearing bleeding arteries, swollen, oozing matter, rotting in their own filth; the patients exhausted with fever and pain. A heavy gloom and sickening odor hung about the dirty wards. Lister was horror-struck.

Glasgow was a large shipbuilding center, and accidents to the poor laborers were frequent. It might be only a deep cut from a tool or a broken leg that brought the worker to the hospital. It was nothing, he might think; in a week, perhaps, he would be back at work. But in a week the wound had become inflamed and swollen, putrid matter would trickle out, a fever set in, and death hovered low.

Lister was torn with this suffering. But his fellow surgeons shrugged their shoulders. "There is nothing strange in this," they assured him. "We expect it. Blood poisoning and hospital gangrene kill half our patients."

"But can nothing be done?"

Again they shrugged. "It is not our fault," they answered complacently. "You see, the wound itself may be simple, but the oxygen in the air . . ."

"The oxygen?"

"Yes."

"Why? What does it do to the wound?"

"Oh," they made vague gestures. "Something or other. It inflames it."

Lister was dumbfounded. What had the air to do with it? If it really was the air, then there was no hope. We cannot exclude the air. The workers in Glasgow must perish by hundreds. Industry must stop, for the air in a hospital did "something or other" that was fatal.

Lister could not believe it was the air, but he noticed one thing. If a patient came with a broken leg and the outer skin had not been cut, he recovered. But if the outer skin was severed and the wound an open one, the patient was doomed. At that very moment, Pasteur was observing that when a fruit had its skin bruised, it became rotten at once.

"These hospital diseases, gangrene and blood poisoning!" exclaimed one surgeon. "Take the patient out of the hospital if you would have him recover. Take him to the church! Take him to the schoolroom! Take him to the stable! Anywhere but to the hospital, for that will be his grave!"

II

One day in June, Lister, very much depressed, was walking home with his friend Tom Anderson, who taught chemistry.

"I can't understand it," worried Lister. "I suppose I never shall understand it. A wound putrefies. Why? I cannot help thinking that the man who is able to explain this problem will gain the world's undying blessing."

"Don't be discouraged," his friend said. "You may be the man." And then as if by a happy chance, he asked, "Have you read the papers of Louis Pasteur?"

"No, who is he?"

"A French chemist who has written very brilliantly on the subject of fermentation. He says that there are microbes . . ."

Thus Lister came to know of Pasteur's theory. Like a vast white light, Pasteur's words flooded him. Like a germ the theory infected him, driving him to tramp restlessly in the night air, struggling on the verge of a discovery. His heart leaping, he said, "The same thing that sours milk and ferments the crushed grapes must also rot the raw flesh and putrefy it. Microbes! Not the air but the dust in the air, bearing this tiniest creature to do its deadly work; or the hands of the surgeon, carrying the bacteria from one wound to another."

"Microbes . . ." he gravely told the other doctors.

Really, they thought, it was a pity that a fine fellow like Lister should take the crazy Frenchman so seriously.

"Microbes," he went on unafraid, "are like vultures hovering over a fallen body. Bacteria are more deadly than bullets."

"Yes, yes," they said sarcastically.

But he did not mind their thrusts, the gentle soul; he pondered how to kill the bacteria in a wound and then to prevent them from entering. That was a tough problem. It did no good to know a fault, if one were not able to correct it.

One day Lister saw this heading in a newspaper:

CITY OF CARLISLE GETS RID OF SEWAGE
CARBOLIC ACID SPRINKLED ON SEWAGE KILLS ODOR

He was off to Carlisle in an instant, to make sure. "The fetid odor of sewage," he reasoned, "is like the fetid odor of a putrefied wound. Both spell bacteria. No odor, no bacteria. What kills one, kills the other."

He forged the first great antiseptic weapon: carbolic acid. The doom of the microbe was at hand.

III

A year later a startling contrast set the world agape. There were two accident wards in the Glasgow hospi-

tal. In one, as of old, the air killed many; the agony was
so heartrending that the ward had to be closed. In the
other, separated from the former by a corridor only
twelve feet wide, there had not been a single case of
blood poisoning or hospital gangrene. That was Lister's
ward.

The astounded world flocked to Glasgow to congrat-
ulate Lister, to do him honor, and to learn from him.
"I have done nothing," he said with sincere modesty,
"but the antiseptic treatment does wonders. I keep a
wound saturated with a mild solution of carbolic acid.
That kills the microbes, and keeps the wound fresh and
sweet. Nature does the rest."

They watched him at work. What a different place
his ward was from the old hospital room! Instead of the
fetid odor of decaying flesh, fresh air prevailed and the
sunshine came cheerily in. Instead of patients with
wan, pinched faces, praying for death to deliver them
from pain, these patients were radiant with hope and
relief. Instead of being carried out in coffins, they
walked out, restored in health. Instead of fear of the
surgeon, they felt a boundless gratitude for his blessed
hands.

"He likes the little yins best and the auld women,"
whispered a street urchin as Lister passed his bed.

In later life, his students said that contact with him
was of the best and purest in life. The only time a rebuke was known to come from his lips was when a
young student of his lifted a broken leg a little too
roughly. "A feeling heart is the first requisite of a surgeon," he said.

To the poor he was as tender as to the rich. He operated on Queen Victoria and the humblest beggar with the same care. The famous poet William Henley, who was a patient of his, was inspired to write a beautiful sonnet about him, called "The Chief," which closes with the lines:

> *His wise, rare smile is sweet with certainties,*
> *And seems in all his patients to compel*
> *Such love and faith as failure cannot quell;*
> *We hold him for another Heracles,*
> *Battling with custom, prejudice, disease,*
> *At once the Son of Zeus with Death and Hell.*

The whole world paid him homage. The queen knighted him; he was appointed to the House of Lords — but all this meant nothing to the man who had given up riches that he might devote himself to the mighty task of destroying pain and disease. This he did as only a handful of men in the history of the world have done. If it had not been for Lister, every year thousands would be dying. The hospital of today, surgery of today, we owe to him.

"Why do you talk of germs!" was rudely demanded of Pasteur. "What are they? Show them to us."

And although stormy debaters surrounded Pasteur and shattered his nerves, Lister did not need to be convinced. He saw in a flash. Always modest, he wrote to Pasteur: "Allow me to tender you my cordial thanks for having demonstrated to me the truth of the germ theory of putrefaction, and then furnished me with the principle upon which alone the antiseptic system can be carried out."

At the Pasteur Jubilee in 1892 in Paris, Lister arose and turning to the old Frenchman said, "Thanks to you, surgery has been stripped of its ancient terrors and has thus enlarged without limits its power."

At these words, Pasteur could not contain himself. Springing up, he hurried to Lister and taking him like a child by the hand, led him to the center of the platform and there embraced him, while the spectators thundered applause and shed tears at the sight of those two brothers in science who were laboring to lessen the sorrows of human life.

IV

Before Lister, the greatest surgeon was a remarkable Frenchman, Ambroise Paré, who lived in the sixteenth century. It was Paré who dreamed of changing surgery from the terror that it was and the last hope of the dying man, into a way of healing. It was Lister who completed Paré's work and at last made the dream come true.

Paré was the medical genius of his day. Prince and pauper alike were happier because he lived. But his fellow surgeons were bewildered. In every meeting of doctors, his amazing career was rehearsed, somewhat as follows:

First Physician: Say! Have you heard about that surgeon in the army of our King Francis?
Second Physician: No, what about him?
First Physician: He has discovered a new way of dressing wounds.
Second Physician: Really! Is he a member of one of the surgeon guilds?

First Physician: That is the amazing thing. He is only a barber-surgeon.

Second Physician: But what can a barber know? He might know the remedy every soldier uses for gunshot wounds — that drink of gunpowder stirred in water — but . . . Can this barber read Latin?

First Physician: No. He admits he knows neither Latin nor Greek.

Second Physician: Then how did he study his Galen? What can be his discovery?

First Physician: I'm coming to that. You see, he was apprenticed in the usual way to a barber. Like all apprentices he swept and opened the shop at daybreak. Then he would comb wigs, singe beards, and shave. Toward evening he might want to read. But even then, you may imagine, a customer might interrupt to have his hair cut.

Second Physician: Well, when did he learn surgery?

First Physician: Do you not know that the University Professors are kind enough to lecture to apprentices in the small hours of the dawn?

Second Physician: Certainly, but lectures are in Latin. It is below the dignity of a physician to lecture in the language of the common people. You said he knew no Latin.

First Physician: Oh, probably some one explained to him what the professor said.

Second Physician: Probably. You still have not told me what great discovery this Paré made.

First Physician: I'm coming to that. Well, he joined the army. There he learned his surgery by using his eyes and his hands. Don't laugh. He managed to learn something that way. He learned, for instance, that you treat gunshot wounds by scalding them with the painful oil of elders.

Second Physician: In the name of Esculapius! What did he discover?

First Physician: I'm coming to that. Once he happened to run short of oil, when he had some wounds to dress. He was in a panic. They say, you see, he is a very kind soul. But what could he do? He was forced to apply something else to the soldiers' wounds. Here is his discovery. He made a mixture of the yolk of eggs, oil of rose, and turpentine and applied that instead.

That night he could not sleep. You see, he was thinking, "I should have made that mixture scalding hot. I shall certainly find my poor patients dead." But in the morning strangely enough . . . You see . . . Well, well! Don't get angry. I'm coming to it. Paré found that those whom he treated with his new mixture had but little pain, and their wounds were without inflammation or swelling. They had rested fairly well that night, and were recovering. But the others, on whom the boiling oil was used, were feverish with great pain and swelling about the edges of their wounds. That is his discovery: never more to scald a poor patient suffering from a gunshot wound.

Second Physician: So! But that was accidental. I wouldn't say Paré made a great discovery.

First Physician: Oh, forgive me. That is not the discovery I was going to tell you about. That is not the *great* discovery. You see, for instance, he heard of a surgeon famous for his treatment of gunshot wounds. Paré wanted to learn the treatment, but the greedy surgeon would not tell. For two whole years Paré coaxed. You see, he wanted to know everything. And who could tell him? Maybe the secret was worthwhile. At last, thanks to his persistence and his presents, Paré got the cure from the scoundrel: take oil of lilies, earthworms soaked in turpentine, and whelps just born. Boil these together! You may imagine that such twaddle did not satisfy Paré.

Second Physician: But how about the *great* discovery?

First Physician: Oh yes. I was just coming to it. He had to find some way to stop the flow of blood when a limb was amputated. Paré says that two out of every three die because they lose so much blood during the amputation.

Second Physician: Nonsense! A red-hot iron will wither the artery, and the blood will no longer flow.

First Physician: But think of the horrible suffering! Even those who do escape death are sick for a long time, and the wounds thus burned are slow to heal. For the burning causes such vehement pains that the patients fall into fever and convulsions. And in most cases, when the scar falls off, bleeding starts afresh. What do you do then? Stanch the blood again with a red-hot iron? Why, the flesh is seared to the bare bone, so that healing is impossible. And in such cases, ulcers develop and make the end of the patient's life an agony.

Second Physician: Will you or will you not tell me the great discovery?

First Physician: Now I've come to it. Instead of sealing up the artery by burning, Paré simply ties it. The blood no longer flows, and the patient is no longer doomed.

For three hundred years after Paré no further progress was made. Yet the piece of silk tied round the cut end of an artery had a great fault, as Lister found. It was not free from germs. Pus formed and kept on forming until the silk cord was removed. This was done by leaving the long ends of the cord hanging, so that, when the knot had rotted away through the artery, the silk cord was pulled out. Meanwhile, the patient's strength wasted away under the infection, and death was almost inevitable.

Doctors were in despair. When they amputated, they must go back, it seemed, to the barbarism of burning the artery. Then came Lister, with his belief in germs and his simple weapon of carbolic acid.

Once he was treating a man for a fracture of a bone. As usual, he washed the wound with carbolic acid. Looking closely one day under the crust formed on the wound he saw a tiny cavity, filled with a brownish fluid. As Lister touched the edge of the crust, it began to bleed!

"How can the crust bleed?" Lister wondered. "It is not flesh."

But it was. The healthy, live tissue around the crust had begun to grow, and had eaten up the dead matter. "If living tissue can eat up dead blood crust," cried Lister, "why should it not eat up the silk cord with which I tie the artery? My carbolic acid will keep it free from microbes. I won't need long threads left hanging out of wounds. I shall cut the ends short. The wound will close, and the silk binding will be absorbed by the living tissue around it."

That is exactly what happened. The silk ligature disappeared very slowly.

"Silk is not the best material for ligatures. I must try something else." He chose catgut, finally, a thread made from the small intestines of a sheep. He tied an artery with it. Shortly, the gray of the catgut turned to pink. The flesh had digested the gut very easily. Lister had succeeded.

Today the surgeon who ties an artery with catgut is thankful to Lister. And the feeling of mankind for the great man was well expressed by Mr. Bayard, the American Ambassador, at a banquet the Royal Society once gave in Lord Lister's honor: "My Lord, it is not a profession, it is not a nation, it is humanity itself which, with uncovered head, salutes you."

William Crawford Gorgas

(1854–1920)

A DIFFERENT KIND OF SOLDIER

I

AT BREAK OF DAY a message was sent to Dr. Gorgas. "Her Ladyship is in a critical condition. Come at once," the message said. Dr. Gorgas dressed hurriedly, and soon arrived at her home, a large glass jar. He found Her Ladyship lying on a bed of cotton wool surrounded by several nurses. She was very beautiful; her body was marked by silver half-moons; her thorax, by four brilliant stripes; and her legs were striped black and white.

Her Ladyship was beyond the pale of medical science. That evening she finally died with as many doctors and nurses attending her as befitted her station in life.

For she had been a member of an aristocratic family, the Stegomyia, the most important mosquito in the world — the mosquito which carries the yellow-fever germ in its body. When it bites you, it leaves the germ with you; and then death is not far distant. Her Ladyship had been probably the most vicious of her kind. In her little body she had carried the yellow-fever germ around so long that she had become a living laboratory of the disease, which the doctors were then studying. Therefore Dr. William Gorgas and his associate, Dr. Walter Reed, mourned Her Ladyship.

The yellow-fever germ has played a greater role in history than many a king. For human slaughter it is more illustrious than Attila or Genghis Khan. On the island of Santa Lucia in 1664, for instance, all but a handful of men out of an army of about ten thousand perished without so much as knowing the real enemy.

Once by itself it was the unconquerable army and navy of the West Indies. In 1762 an expedition of English and Colonial forces seized Cuba. After a few months' occupation, the force was utterly routed — by the yellow-fever germ. In 1800, Napoleon sent his best forces to Haiti. In less than a year, the army, with livid faces and black vomitings, was destroyed. Guns were of no avail; soldiers served only to fill graves, and the inhuman enemy remained invisible and majestic. Yellow fever was the real reason why Napoleon sold us Louisiana.

In 1793, a yellow-fever epidemic broke out in Philadelphia. There was scarcely a home without its dead member. Unburied bodies lay in the streets. Everybody who could fled from the stricken city. Yet the toll was four thousand lives.

In 1882, the yellow-fever germ made a fatal mistake, for which it eventually paid with its life; it attacked William Gorgas and failed to kill him. This made him immune, in the way Pasteur had discovered.

As a child William wanted to be a soldier. But in his

manhood he realized that the greatest war was again disease and ignorance. Therefore he decided to be a doctor. It was the time of Pasteur, Koch, and Lister. "Look for the germ," was the cry, and Gorgas took it up. He was, besides, one of the first surgeons to practice Listerism in America.

II

Our country had suddenly awakened to a grave trouble. The Americans had defeated the Spanish army in Cuba, and had established an independent Cuba. The American army was on the point of withdrawal when a new enemy attacked the soldiers. Languor and chilliness seized the men, headaches and muscular pains. "Notice the peculiar look of the eyes, the flush on the face, the scarlet tongue. Yellow fever!"

Then came the fever heat, with its thirst and hot skin, its restlessness and its delirium. Anxiously the doctors waited for the next stage of the illness — the cold skin, lemon yellow in tint. Would the patients recover or must they die? Cuba, it seemed, would have to be abandoned to that invincible enemy — the yellow-fever germ.

In despair the government had sent Gorgas and a few other soldiers of science to Havana. The shadow of gloom, however, came over Gorgas and his fellow doctors, who were ready to give their lives for the cause. And there was good reason for gloom. Dr. Gorgas had seen that the putrid streets of Havana were made spotlessly clean, and proper sewerage built. The stinking city, over which had hovered black vultures swooping down on the filth, had changed its dress and was for once spotlessly clean. Why then did yellow fever continue to mock the labors of Gorgas? The pestilence had grown worse, if anything.

"You have failed," said an old doctor to him, "and you will fail. Listen to me. The cursed mosquito, the Stegomyia kind, is at the bottom of the trouble. I can't prove it, but I *know* I'm right. It's the mosquito."

Gorgas listened doubtfully, but he thought: "There may be something in this idea about mosquitoes. Let us find out."

"I'll let the mosquito bite me," said his friend Dr. Reed, "and if I fall victim to yellow fever, you, Gorgas, will know how to carry on the fight."

But the government would not allow this; Dr. Reed's life was too valuable. It was useless for Gorgas to offer himself because he was immune. Two other doctors of the heroic band, however, thought, "How can we die better than in the cause of science?" And they let a mosquito which had bitten a yellow-fever patient bite them, too. In a few days they were in the clutch of death.

Perhaps it was true then. Perhaps the Stegomyia mosquito did carry the yellow-fever germ from one person to another. But it was not certain yet. Maybe the two victims had caught yellow fever elsewhere. More men were needed for this dangerous experiment. A call for heroes was sent out, "You who are willing to sacrifice your live that humanity may be free from the curse of the yellow fever, where are you?"

Into Dr. Reed's office one day stepped two unknown men. They were just plain citizens from Ohio, just plain John Kissinger and James Moran. They were willing to help, they said simply, if they could be of any use.

"You realize what you are doing, don't you?" warned Walter Reed. "You may die."

Kissinger and Moran nodded. They knew that. They were quite willing. Two more heroes had entered the struggle to aid humanity.

Both men were secluded in a house for weeks, to make sure they could not contract the fever in any other way. Then the dreaded Stegomyia mosquito was let in to stick its proboscis into their flesh. Three days later the already overcrowded yellow-fever ward received two new patients, John Kissinger and James Moran.

There was no doubt now in the mind of Gorgas and his band, but everybody else was scornful. A mosquito, so weak and little! Ridiculous!

The people were gloomier than ever. "Even if it is true," they said, "what good does it do to know that mosquitoes deal death? We cannot get rid of them. We might as well try to get rid of the air."

But William Gorgas was a determined man. "If it is the mosquito," he said simply, "we *will* get rid of it."

He was jeered roundly. "What! You want us to act like lunatics, hunting mosquitoes? Be reasonable! Besides, we can't kill all the mosquitoes in the world."

"Perhaps not," he replied quietly, "but we can try."

He began warily to study the habits of the enemy. He found that the Stegomyia mosquito is a tame insect. It will not live away from human beings. It refuses to lay its eggs anywhere but around a house, in a container of water.

"Swatting the mosquito will not answer," reasoned Gorgas. "I must strike the mosquito at its source — by destroying its eggs. Then no mosquitoes will hatch. But how can I crush these minute specks floating on water?"

Here was a puzzle indeed: to wage war against an unseen foe. Gorgas pursued the matter: "What is the weak spot of the enemy? There one should strike. The more we know about his habits, the easier will it be for us to win."

"Instead of stamping out yellow fever, Gorgas studies mosquitoes," some government officials muttered. "As if an insect could have anything to do with disease!"

But Gorgas was learning many curious things about the mosquito. He found that the mosquito egg first hatches into a wormlike wriggler, which lives in the water. The wriggler grows until it is about a quarter of an inch long; then it changes to a mosquito. One day, as he watched these wrigglers, Gorgas discovered the weak spot of the enemy. The wrigglers had to come to the surface of the water for air.

His heart beat fast as he realized that at last he held the key to the problem. "If I prevent these wrigglers from coming to the surface of the water, they will suffocate. Now, how can I prevent this? How can I cover the water?"

With oil! That answer came to him. "Oil and water do not mix. The oil stays on top. It will not spoil the water for us, therefore, and to a wriggler it will be like an iron wall between him and air. A little oil on the water and the imprisoned wrigglers will soon die. Then there will be no mosquitoes, and no yellow fever."

"Leave no container of water uncovered. Pour a little oil on all standing water," was his order.

"Never leave a basin of water standing!" exclaimed the Cubans. "Gorgas is crazy. We will do what we please about it."

But Gorgas was a kind man. He did not order them to act, although he had the authority to order. He simply explained, showed how such a procedure was for their own good, and pleaded with them as a friend to trust him. The Cubans loved and respected him for this kindness, and devotedly they helped him.

Gorgas organized a health army. The soldiers were inspectors; their weapons, pails of kerosene. In every district, you could see the inspector armed with a pail of kerosene, looking for tin cans, water barrels, and tanks. Every building in Havana was visited each month, and every possible place in it where water might have gathered was carefully searched.

"Your work is useless," a doctor from Havana told Gorgas.

"What makes you think so?" asked Gorgas.

"I've emptied every container of water in my house. Yet there are plenty of mosquitoes."

"Let us look," suggested Gorgas calmly.

Sure enough, after a long search Gorgas discovered a small pail half full of water, tucked away, unsuspected, in a closet.

The task of destroying all the mosquitoes in Havana was indeed tremendous. Yet Gorgas and his friend Dr.

Reed succeeded perfectly. A few figures, and the story of Gorgas comes to a happy ending. Before the time of Gorgas, for about one hundred and fifty years, there was not a day without a case of yellow fever in Havana. In 1896, there were twelve hundred eighty-two deaths. Since these heroes won their campaign, there has not been a single case of yellow fever on record there.

III

After Cuba, Panama was the problem facing the United States. The French had failed to construct a canal there, because yellow fever had destroyed its workers as fast as they were sent. And now the United States had possession.

To go to work in Panama was almost like committing suicide. Workers coming from America sometimes brought along their coffins. Funeral trains were more common than freight or passenger trains. The horror grew so great that it seemed as though the Atlantic and Pacific Oceans would never be joined; that Panama would have to remain the jungle home of beasts and snakes. The Stegomyia was doing its terrible best.

The president dispatched the great yellow-fever fighter to Panama. Everything depended on Gorgas. But to the admiral in charge of Panama this great man and his mosquito theory was a joke. Gorgas was hindered and checked wherever he went. He was refused supplies and, despite his warnings, was disobeyed and ridiculed.

In November, 1904, the fun started. The lurking

Stegomyia was on the warpath. Officials and laborers were in the trap together. Work on the Canal stopped. Those who could fled in terror, only to be caught in their tracks. New arrivals from the United States sailed home the same day they arrived. The loss of life was pitiable. Gorgas could but watch sorrowfully. The Canal seemed doomed.

Humbly the officials turned to him. Now they heeded Gorgas in every order: "No exposed containers of water. Beware the mosquito."

The disease began to slacken its pace. Its victims became fewer and fewer, until one beautiful day in 1905, the final case of yellow fever was over in the Isthmus. Gorgas had at last wrested the Panama Canal from its ancient lord, yellow fever. His prophecy has been fulfilled. The Canal has been built, and from 1905 to this day not a single case of yellow fever has been contracted there.

IV

The final chapter in the story of yellow fever is one of tragic glory. Yellow fever and its evil sign, the black vomit, troubles us no more, but in the last and greatest struggle with it, Hideyo Noguchi, the Japanese hero, gave his life.

It happened in this way. The yellow-fever germ had come, ravished millions of lives, and then been driven off by Dr. Gorgas and his band. But as yet no one had ever seen the germ. "Look for the germ," had counseled Pasteur. Gorgas and every other scientist had looked for the yellow-fever germ, but in vain. It remained invisible. Doctors began to doubt that there was a germ causing the black vomit.

"Maybe Pasteur has gone too far. Maybe there are some diseases which are not caused by a germ. Yellow fever, perhaps, is caused by the Stegomyia mosquito itself."

The great scientists did not doubt; they believed in Pasteur. That caused them to be worried by the invisible germ of yellow fever.

"No," Gorgas had said, "the mosquito is an innocent host, which gives lodging to the real criminal. For some reason this invisible germ lives best in the body of the mosquito. Then, when his host lights on human skin to sip a bit of blood, out slips the germ to do its deadly work."

"Well," replied the doubters, "prove it. Show us the germ."

That none could do, and there the mystery hung for a while.

In 1918, the province in Ecuador called Guayaquil sent out a cry of distress. It was the old story. The invisible peril had laid its hand heavily on the people of Guayaquil and was spreading its destruction. Again the black vomit: again the strewn bodies.

In America the Rockefeller Institute heard the cry and sent down a little group, among whom was the brilliant doctor Hideyo Noguchi.

Just about the time when Pasteur was working on the cure for rabies and Gorgas was poring over his medical books at college, Hideyo Noguchi was born in a small town in Japan. His home was a hovel, and had it not been for the charity of a friend, he would never have gone to the schools in Tokyo and later in America. He showed such remarkable power as a student that the charitable friend thought it would be a pity not to help him on until he became a doctor. But he was more than an ordinary physician. He gained such knowledge in the science of disease that the Rockefeller Institute invited him to work on its great problems. And what a worker he proved to be! Once he started on an experiment, his friends knew, there was no use trying to lure him out of his laboratory. He scarcely ate or slept.

So, with his test tubes and microscope and a crate of guinea pigs, he landed in Ecuador.

"Gorgas was right," he at once remarked. "First of all, death to the mosquito! And as for your sick ones — do not move them, and give them no food and plenty of water."

The scene in Havana and Panama repeated itself in Ecuador. "No standing water!" was the order. And good inspectors were there, too, to see the order carried out.

Meanwhile Noguchi was working in his laboratory at the seemingly impossible task of finding the germ. He let one of his guinea pigs contract yellow fever. Then he took some of its diseased blood, filtered it, and thought, "Now the germ ought to be on the filter." When he put the filter under the microscope, however, there was as usual no sign of the elusive germ.

"An impossible task!" he seemed to hear repeated.

Suddenly it flashed into the mind of Hideyo Noguchi that perhaps the germ is so small that it slips through the filter. "No wonder we haven't found the germ," he cried. "Perhaps we have been looking in the wrong place. Besides, it may be so small that the ordinary microscope fails to show it."

So he proved. Before long, using what is known as a dark-field microscope, he was able to unmask the wriggling pest.

"Now," thought Noguchi, elated, "let us turn this villain of the centuries into its own enemy. Let us see about making a vaccine of it, as Jenner did with smallpox, to prevent yellow fever, and then a serum to cure it."

He had the vaccine ready in a short while. "Will it work, though?" was his anxious question. The test was before him. He vaccinated about one thousand soldiers and sent them into Guayaquil where the disease was still raging. And the results?

"Noguchi," his comrades said warmly, "you have won. You have conquered yellow fever."

"But the results?" he inquired impatiently.

"Only eleven of the one thousand soldiers have contracted the disease. Congratulations!"

"No, no!" protested Noguchi. "I have not succeeded. I have failed."

Back he went to his laboratory. "The vaccine must be stronger," he decided.

During the years 1920 and 1921, ten thousand people in the yellow-fever districts of Mexico, Salvador, Guatemala, and the British Honduras were vaccinated with Noguchi's new vaccine. And the results? Every one of the ten thousand remained safe. Noguchi saved them — and millions after them.

In gratitude the government of Ecuador offered him a large estate and a fine laboratory if he would only consent to stay with them. Noguchi refused. There was more work to be done. He returned to the United States. But in Ecuador there is a Calle Noguchi, and a bronze momument has been raised to him. Not only through Ecuador did his name ring. The whole world celebrated his success.

What Noguchi had done for yellow fever, he now set out to do for hydrophobia. For that disease Pasteur had found the cure but, just as in the case of yellow fever, the germ of rabies had defied detection. It continued to attack and retreat in a cloak of invisibility. That was before Noguchi began his work of hunting it down. It does so no longer.

"There!" Noguchi was able to cry, pointing to the swarm of hydrophobia germs under his microscope. "There is the terrible pest, helpless at last."

So the labors of Pasteur and Gorgas both were turned into complete triumph by Noguchi.

All at once, in 1927, the shadow of death fell upon a large area on the west coast of Africa.

"Yellow fever is abroad again," the doctors in Accra cabled. "But it is not the yellow fever that we know. It is in a strange guise, or perhaps it is a cousin to the black vomit of America. We do not know, and we are helpless."

There was one man to whom every one looked — Hideyo Noguchi. And he was ready to go.

He had been working hard, and as he said farewell to his friends, he seemed a bit tired and his eyes flashed a little more brilliantly than usual.

"Perhaps he should not go at this time," thought his friends uneasily. "At least not to Accra, which is one of the most unhealthy spots in the world."

They waited for news, and the worst came. The great man had hardly been welcomed in Accra, he had hardly begun his work, when he was stricken down. He who had saved so many millions of people had not now the strength to fight for himself. He died on May 21, 1928, a martyr to the cause of science and humanity. His triumph was in bringing to completion the work of General William Crawford Gorgas.

Elie Metchnikoff

(1845–1916)

OUR BODY'S DEFENDERS

I

To his parents Elie seemed full of contradictions: a nature sweet and gentle, yet moody and lonely as the steppes beyond the Metchnikoff estate in the Russian province of Kharkov; a mind brilliant but undisciplined. He loved music, especially the music of Mozart and Beethoven, yet refused to practice the piano. He read difficult books on science but was scornful of the school he attended. Finally, when his parents expected him to enter the nearby Kharkov University he insisted that he must go abroad to pursue his studies.

His father tried to reason with him. "I am not rich. I don't see why you can't stay in Kharkov."

"Father, I can't learn science from books alone. I want to be a zoologist. I must go where there are good laboratories. The best are in Germany. At the University of Würzburg I could study under the great Professor Koelliker."

The youth seemed to know what he wanted and his father yielded. Nevertheless, here is what happened:

The seventeen-year-old Elie took the train first to

Leipzig in order to buy the books he needed. He arrived late in the evening. The streets were dark, the city strange. People passed by, without regard for him. It suddenly struck him that he was alone and very far from home. A tremor of fear ran through him.

A man was looking at him. The man came nearer. Elie restrained an impulse to run. *"Was gibt's, Junge?"* The tone of the man was kindly and in a rush of broken German Elie told him his plight.

"Come," said the sympathetic stranger. "My family will put you up for the night. Tomorrow we'll see."

Early next morning Elie was in the street waiting for the bookshops to open. When he bought the books he needed he turned to go back to the house where his luggage was. Now where was it? He had failed to note the address. Lost, he wandered about the city of Leipzig. Fortunately it was not a big city and by the close of day he found the house.

At Würzburg he was not so lucky. It turned out that he had neglected to note when classes were in session, and he arrived during vacation. Once again he was stranded. He engaged a room and dragged his luggage in. In the midst of unpacking he was seized with a feeling of loathing for the room, for Würzburg, for Germany, for the world of science. His heart was breaking with homesickness. He grabbed up his luggage, rushed off to the railroad station and took the first train home. The University of Kharkov it was to be, after all.

The contradiction in his nature continued to express itself. As a student he made so brilliant a record that at twenty-two he was appointed professor of biology at the University of Odessa. He was popular with both students and faculty. Yet he resigned his post in protest against the czar-like tyranny of the university officials. Elie Metchnikoff believed in freedom for the individual, the czar's government did not. But when Elie, in Switzerland, fell in with a group of Russian exiles who preached revolution, he was horrified at the thought of violence and bloodshed. As he had walked out of the czar-ridden university, so now he parted company with the bloodthirsty exiles. It saddened him to think that the forces of destruction and death were at war with the forces of creative life.

Within himself, too, the war was going on. Often a mood of despair gripped him. When his young wife died he was overcome by grief. "If sooner or later all things must die," he thought hopelessly, "the sooner the better." What had he to live for? Death had taken his only companion. His one remaining consolation, scientific research, was about to be taken from him because his eyes were growing weak. The last thing left was the means to put an end to himself.

He was staying at a hotel in Geneva. Among his things was a bottle of poison. But when he swallowed it the healthy forces within him spewed it out and he found himself still among the living. His mind, however, was still poisoned by despair. It was a cold night. After a steaming bath he rushed out toward the lake, his chest uncovered. The microbes of pneumonia, he hoped, would be more cooperative than the poison.

The Rhone bridge was lit by a streetlamp. Around the lamp insects were swarming. "Ephemeridae," reflected the professor. "They do not eat. They live only a few hours." A question came to mind. "They do not have the time to adapt themselves to their environment. How then can Darwin's theory of natural selection apply to them? Ah, there's a problem worth tackling . . . Heavens, but it's cold."

Intent on the problem he forgot his morbid thoughts and hurried back to the hotel.

II

The despair and indecision of youth were over. His eyesight improved and he no longer had to fear blindness. He remarried. Life was good.

His researches culminated in 1882 in a famous discovery. He happened to be interested in the process of digestion among very primitive creatures. He was then living in Messina on the northern coast of Sicily, and was looking into the transparent bodies of starfish.

One morning he was examining under his microscope a specimen of a starfish. The fragrance of tropical flowers came in from the garden and he could hear the sea lapping on the sands beyond. The family were in town attending a circus. They couldn't have been more fascinated than was Elie Metchnikoff. He had prodded into the outer layer of the transparent flesh of the starfish a few grains of a dried insect. A queer process was going on. From the body of the starfish tiny round cells were detaching themselves. They did not float about aimlessly. They seemed motivated. They made their way toward the intruded grains, surrounded them, and engulfed them.

"Is this how the starfish digests food?" he wondered.

He hurried into the garden. From a tangerine tree

he cut a few thorns. These he poked into the outer layer of the flesh. "If these cells attack the thorns it can't be for nourishment," he thought. "It must be for some other reason. What other reason can there be but defense?"

He had to wait till morning to know the answer. During the night it occurred to him that much more depended on his simple experiment than a discovery about the welfare of the tribe of starfish. He thought of a person running a splinter of wood into his finger. Would his experiment shed any light on the natural defense in man's body?

He was too excited to sleep. At the first streak of dawn he jumped out of bed and ran to his workroom. He put his eye to the microscope. A shout escaped him and his wife, alarmed, came running in.

"The thorns are gone," he cried. "That settles it. Those cells are the body's defenders, as I suspected. They devour intruders. They are the home defense against invaders."

To verify his discovery he made a number of experiments using mice and frogs which he injected with pathogenic (disease-causing) microbes. These confirmed his theory and he announced it.

Every animal, he declared, is equipped with defending cells. If it were not so equipped it could not survive the attack of microbes. In man the defenders are the white corpuscles which migrate through the walls of blood vessels to counterattack an invading body, be it a splinter of wood or a microbe. Like a well-trained army mobilized for action the white corpuscles hurl themselves on the invaders. The field of battle becomes inflamed. The wounded corpuscles turn to pus. If the defending cells are destroyed by the microbes, the body may die. If the victory goes to the cells, the body is cured. Metchnikoff called the white corpuscles phagocytes, which means "cells that eat."

Now he was able to explain why vaccines protected the body against disease. A vaccine is made of weakened or killed microbes. When it is injected into the bloodstream the phagocytes have an easy time in the battle. They are thus trained and strengthened and well prepared for the real fight.

Like all scientific theories when first announced, Metchnikoff's theory of phagocytes was greeted with doubt and skepticism. That was proper. Before being acceped a new theory must be challenged to undergo many tests. The phagocyte theory survived the tests.

Among the first to hail the discovery was the great Louis Pasteur, who offered Metchnikoff a laboratory at the Pasteur Institute in Paris. Metchnikoff accepted gladly. He and Louis Pasteur became fast friends, and he passed the rest of his days as biologist and teacher in the Institute. Often the older scientist attended the lectures of the younger.

"Man," Metchnikoff taught, "carries within his body many deadly germs. Against these not only do the phagocytes protect him, but other microbes, friendly kinds." To demonstrate, he sometimes turned to one of his students and said: "There are influenza germs in your mouth and nose right now. Let me show you."

He asked the startled young man to put a specimen of mucus under the microscope and, sure enough, there were the pathogenic microbes. Metchnikoff smiled and said: "You're none the worse for harboring them. Why not? Because of the friendly microbes which you entertain at the same time. The friendly ones stave off the hostile ones.

"Good health is a question of protecting ourselves against hostile microbes. Science may some day rid us of all disease. I dream of science overcoming death itself, or at any rate of delaying it until it comes as welcome to the person as the deep sleep at the day's end."

"How could such a thing ever be possible?" his students asked.

Metchnikoff explained: "Old age comes when the cells in the body's tissues grow weak. Then the phagocytes may turn traitors and devour the cells as they were wont to do to enemy microbes. I have seen the phagocytes of a tadpole eat its tail up as the tadpole turned into a frog which needs no tail since it has legs."

"What makes the cells weak?"

"Hostile microbes hiding in a place safe from the phagocytes. Usually the place is the large intestine. From this hiding place they distill their slow poison which weakens the cells of the body."

"And the cure?"

"To introduce into the camp of the enemy, the large intestine, other microbes, friendly ones."

Elie Metchnikoff believed that a long and healthy life depended on proper diet. As vaccines strengthened phagocytes in the bloodstream, so proper diet strengthened colonies of friendly bacteria in the bowel.

"Strengthen the body's defenses."

This was Elie Metchnikoff's scientific creed. He worked and urged his colleagues to work so that the span of human life would be extended and the time of death put off. Science, he hoped, would some day make it possible for everyone to reach his life's goal.

Metchnikoff himself lived in the light of the philosophy. He worked hard and always in the interest of his fellow man. When at the age of seventy-one he felt the approach of death his chief concern was to assuage the grief of his wife. When she seemed to accept his passing away he said: "Now I am ready."

Charles Darwin
(*1809–1882*)
and Charles Lyell
(*1797–1875*)

EVOLUTION

I

As BOYS it was not possible for them to be acquainted. In 1809 Charles Lyell was almost twelve, Charles Darwin just born. The first Charles lived in Scotland, not far from Edinburgh, the second Charles three hundred miles away outside London. Charles Lyell went to Oxford to become a lawyer, Charles Darwin to Cambridge intending to become a clergyman. They were far apart and might never have met. What they had in common to bring them together was an overwhelming love of nature. Together they changed the course of science.

Both Charleses grew up in the country. Woods and streams were their natural habitat, the sea and cliffs never far away. They learned the ways of other natives: field mice, beetles, butterflies and birds. Each Charles made his own collection of plants and shells. In this industry Charles Lyell's father encouraged him. But Charles Darwin's father was annoyed by his son's neglect of school homework. "Rat-catcher," Dr. Darwin contemptuously called his son. "You'll be a disgrace to yourself and your family," he predicted. The boy suffered his father's scorn and kept on good terms with the wild creatures. Once, on tearing off some old bark from a tree, he uncovered two rare beetles. He seized one in each hand. Just then he saw a third beetle. He popped the one he held in his right hand into his mouth. The beetle ejected a burning fluid. Charles spat and lost two beetles.

Charles Lyell had blue eyes, chiseled features and blond hair. He was hesitant of speech, choosing his words carefully. At grammar school he excelled in poetry and bird-nesting. He knew the rules of English composition and the eggs of every bird in the vicinity. He organized a school orchestra in which he played the flute. He had a fistfight with a bully which lasted on and off for two days, after which he was able to stagger back to his room while his opponent had to be carried back.

At Oxford he was a good student of literature. But the moment that changed the direction of his life came from outside his formal studies. It came to him when he opened the pages of a book on geology. An electric streak across the night sky reveals a world different from the ordinary. Such was the effect of his first glimpse of geology upon Charles Lyell.

In the past he had collected stones and shells whose colors caught his fancy. Now he saw beyond the surface of color and shape. A piece of granite made him wonder whether it was igneous rock like basalt. Was it originally spewed up in the fire of a volcano, and cooled and hardened in the atmosphere? Or was it like

sandstone, built by a sediment of pressed grains of earth?
. . . What caused quakes in the bowels of the earth?
. . . If coal was fossilized plants, how old was the
earth? . . . If you dug into layer below layer of earth
would you be able to trace the story of living things
back to the beginning? . . . What were the forces that
made mountains and lakes, continents and islands?

How old was the earth? On this question scholars
were divided. One side believed that the earth was
about four thousand years old or at most a few thousand more. The other side objected that this was too
short a time to account for the slow building of mountain ranges. High on some slopes were found buried
seashells. This showed that an ocean once covered the
slopes. Judging by the imperceptible rate of change in
shorelines, the age of the earth would have to be measured by millions of years, not thousands. Judging also
by the fossil bones of extinct species of animals, surely
the earth must be many millions of years old.

Yes, said the first side. That would be true if nature
acted uniformly, as you seem to think. But what about
the Flood mentioned in the Bible? Such catastrophes
may have happened more than once. In a single day or
hour the existing world could be destroyed, root and
branch, and a new one seeded.

So the battle was joined, catastrophists against uniformitarians, and plain men did not know what to
make of it. The catastrophists lacked evidence to support their position and fell back upon the Bible. From
this position the uniformitarians did not know how to
dislodge them.

Charles Lyell felt that the issue was of great importance. It dealt with the fate of the world; his world, his fate. He read what all the books said on the subject. But for all that he was little the wiser. As a boy he had raised mice and caterpillars and through his own observations had come to know all their diverse species. He decided to use his legs and explore the earth for himself.

Every holiday he spent walking in parts either of England or Scotland. He inspected stone quarries, climbed up and down mountain gorges and cliffs along the coast. He collected specimens of soil, rocks, and minerals. His experiences raised questions in his mind for which he made it a point to find answers that satisfied his common sense. Question: Why did the Yare River north of Yarmouth turn at right angles? Answer: Because the river could not buck the tide of the sea and had to turn aside, thus cutting a new channel through the land. Question: If England in former epochs was joined to the continent of Europe, how did it become an island? Answer: The force of the north current met the force of the English channel and burst open the straits of Dover. The forces that shaped the earth were purely mechanical, Charles Lyell believed; the effects of heat and frost, the friction of wind and water. The uniformitarians, he decided, were right. There were indeed subterranean pressures which erupted in earthquakes and volcanoes. But such catastrophes were local, not universal. Some people said that science must not contradict the Bible. Charles Lyell believed that the wisdom of the Bible was deeper than its words. As for science, that was simply common sense applied to facts. Whatever explained facts must not contradict common sense. Charles made up his mind also on a more personal matter. He gave up his plan to practice law.

After his third year at Oxford he traveled on the continent touring the mountainous region of France and Italy. His search for the history of the earth now began in earnest. Thanks to his father he had the money to follow clues throughout Europe and North America. He waded in the swamps of Virginia, dug into the coal beds of Nova Scotia, and climbed Mount Etna to watch the flow of lava. On its slopes, seven hundred feet above the sea, he found shells in rock strata one hundred feet thick. They were recent fossils, he judged, no older than a hundred thousand years. On the island of Ischia he found shells showing that the land had risen from the sea, where once it had lain twenty-six hundred feet below the surface. Stranger still, in a cave near Palermo, Sicily, the fossil bones of hyenas and elephants were found. These animals were not among the living fauna of Sicily, and their fossils could be explained only by the theory that the island had once been part of Africa.

Meanwhile, diggings throughout the world were unearthing fossils of gigantic lizard-like animals. Not far from Charles Lyell's home was found the thighbone of an animal that must have been as huge as an elephant. In Bavaria, Germany, fossil remains were discovered of a great bird with a long tail, toothed jaws and toes on the front legs. And near Savannah, Georgia, Charles Lyell examined the skeletons of three monstrous lizards. In the remote past, it seemed, the world was inhabited by a mammoth herbivorous tribe. Names had to be invented for them. The word "fossil" came from the Latin verb "to dig." Now the ancient Greek tongue was drawn upon. Dinosaur means Terrible Lizard. The Savannah find was a Megatherium, which means Great Beast.

In the same strata with the gigantic lizards were found the imprints of plants that could only have lived in a hot climate. Yet — and this was startling — overlying those strata were others that bore the marks of the glaciers. From these strata the giant lizards had disappeared. What had caused the change from a steaming world to a frozen one? Astronomers thought that it might be due to the eccentricity of the earth's orbit around the sun, a turning away from the sun and then back again. This swing took millions of years. Whatever the cause, Charles Lyell was convinced that the earth's age must be measured by hundreds of millions of years.

He was also convinced that species of animals and plants keep changing with time. One species flourishes and dies out; another succeeds it. This one in turn passes and still another replaces it. Now diggings throughout Europe brought to light signs of early man: stone hammers and flints and other crude tools. These were found in the topmost strata. Man, therefore, was the latest arrival. Not that he was just another species of animal. Charles Lyell did not for a moment believe such a thing. No, in the divine scheme of things man was an exception.

It was time, he thought, that someone organized the science of geology. It was raising so many questions about life on earth that it had become more than a hobby for amateurs. Some scholar ought to assemble the facts and show their meaning.

A voice within whispered, "You."

It startled him. "Who, I?"

"Why not? You have been gathering the facts. You have convictions about them."

Charles Lyell was not yet thirty when he began to write his famous *Principles of Geology.*

II

By a lucky chance, just as he was about to sail from England on a voyage lasting five years, Charles Darwin came upon Charles Lyell's book. Likewise by a lucky chance, he found himself on the Royal Navy's ship *Beagle.* The *Beagle,* a 235-ton sloop, ninety feet long, was to circumnavigate the globe, stopping to explore lands distant and wild. For this purpose Captain Fitzroy needed the services of a naturalist. Someone recommended Charles Darwin. He was only twenty-two but — so the captain was told — a good biologist. The offer was made and Charles jumped at it. But his father put down his heavy foot. "Absurd," snorted Dr. Darwin. Then, not to seem too dictatorial, he added, "If you can find even one sensible man who would advise you to go I shall give my consent." The very next day Charles happened to be dining with his uncle Josiah Wedgwood, a very sensible man indeed. "Why," said Uncle Josiah, "it's a splendid idea and I shall tell your father so."

Still, Charles narrowly escaped being rejected. Captain Fitzroy had a curious superstition. He believed that the index to a man's character was his nose.

Charles Darwin was tall and slim. He had brilliant eyes and a high forehead. But as for his nose, the captain disapproved of it. However, after talking a bit with the young naturalist, he decided to take a chance on the nose. In short, one of the happiest events for the history of science, Charles Darwin's voyage on the *Beagle,* depended on the accidents of a dinner and the shape of a nose.

Then there was the accident of Lyell's book reaching him in time to take aboard. For Charles Darwin the book was like a living guide, the spirit of the other Charles directing his attention to the story told in the layers of earth and rock. "Look there," said the guide, "for clues to the history of life on earth."

Charles began a journal of his voyage on the *Beagle.* The first thing he had to record was his being seasick. The *Beagle* pitched through the Bay of Biscay and for ten days the naturalist lay limp in a hammock. Then the winds quieted, the waves calmed down, the sky cleared. Ahead were the Cape Verde Islands. At São Tiago the *Beagle* was anchored and Charles went ashore.

He found himself in another world, or rather in a paradise. Sunshine, palms, tamarinds and bananas. He was transported with delight, and for a time he just luxuriated in the tropical scene. A bird hovered over the water, brown-breasted with a blue-green back. "Halcyon" he was called by the ancient Greeks, who spoke of lovely peaceful days. The bird plunged into a wave and a moment later rose with prey in its beak. This bird lived not by peace but by war against fish. In English his name was kingfisher.

Charles watched a cuttlefish describe arabesques in the water, its ten tentacles waving about. In deep water the color of the cuttlefish was a sort of purple. In shallow water it changed to a yellow-green, but the yellow spots seemed to come and go by turns. Charles bent closer. Stealthily the two creatures approached each other, man and fish. All at once a jet of liquid siphoned from the belly of the fish and spurted into the man's face. The fish vanished in an inky cloud. Charles washed his face and recorded the experience in his journal. He noted that the cuttlefish, like the kingfisher, also lived by his special talents.

Now Charles brought out his geological hammer. On a cliff sixty feet above the sea he came upon a layer of limestone. He cut into it and found shells of some ancient creature of the sea. "Yes," he thought with satisfaction, "the island has risen out of the sea." Charles Lyell had pointed it out to him.

Next landfall was St. Paul's Rocks, off the coast of Brazil, where he saw a crab capture a flying fish. Again that special talent. Now Charles was to explore the mainland, and after landing him the *Beagle* went on, arranging to pick him up at a later date.

The first day he wandered into a Brazilian forest was one of the most thrilling of his life. The twilight alternated with open patches of bright grass and tropical flowers, and stillness with the strident chorus of insects.

The test of Charles's stamina was ahead. Brazil was wild and sparsely populated. Charles hired a guide. They traveled on horseback and usually slept under the stars, Charles like any other seasoned gaucho. Getting enough to eat was quite a problem. Occasionally they happened upon an inn where they were greeted with utmost courtesy. Everyone bowed and the inn-keeper said, "This is your home."

"Thank you. We are famished. Is it possible to procure a meal?"

"Anything you wish, gentlemen."

"Good. We should like a bit of fish."

"Ah, not that."

"Dried beef will do."

"I regret. Not that, either."

"Soup, then."

"There is no soup."

"At least there is bread."

"We have no bread."

"Anything. Anything at all."

After a few hours the starving men asked how much longer they would have to wait.

"It will be ready when it is ready."

Charles Darwin laughed off such hardships. Had comfort and safety been important to him he would have stayed in his wealthy home. He had come to the wilderness to penetrate, if he could, the mystery of nature. As he proceeded through the Brazilian forests into the pampas of the Argentine he met many forms of animal life, all new to him: parrots and monkeys, pumas and condors, tucotucos and capybaras, iguanas and alligators, agoutis and vizcachas.

Two things puzzled him. First, that as he traveled southward every local species of these creatures differed somewhat from the same species in localities he had passed through. Especially was this true if he crossed a mountain range, such as the Andes. In the valley on one side the lizards differed from those on the other. The difference might be small — the shape of the head or the markings on the body — but it was there. He roamed among the islands of the Galápagos. On every one of them there were finches, but from island to island the finches differed in one feature or another.

How did such differences arise? Why did they arise? Near Montevideo Charles found a lizard that was legless except for tiny hind feet. The thought came to him that here was a creature between snake and lizard.

The second puzzle was this: agoutis and vizcachas, for instance, were at home on the grassy pampas of La Plata. Why, then, were they not built like European hares and rabbits, but rather like the rodents of South America? For another instance of the same puzzle: capybaras lived in the swamps and rivers of the forests. Why, then, were they not built like the beavers and muskrats of North America? Why were they, too, built like the rodents in their neighborhood?

The puzzle deepened as he examined fossils. The first, found near Buenos Aires, was that of a great armored beast resembling living species of armadillos. This was followed as he went southward by fossils of gigantic sloths and lizards. In Patagonia he found a camel-like creature with claws. All of these species had become extinct. They resembled living species, yet they had died out. What had happened to extinguish one kind and favor the other? The differences between the two species did not seem great. How had the change come about?

At this point Charles stopped short in his thinking.

"My mind seems to be in a muddle," he thought. "Species don't change." Everyone knew that. Species were fixed, unchangeable, or as scholars put it: species were immutable. "Who am I," thought young Charles Darwin, "to presume to doubt it." Still, as his observations piled up, the faint shadow of a doubt did creep in.

The doubt began with the notion that it would be much easier to explain the differences in species that closely resembled each other if you assumed that species can and do change. The shadow of doubt spread.

He stood on a mountain peak in Tierra del Fuego. Snow was falling. Through the white net of trees he looked down upon a lake. Three natives were gliding to shore in a canoe. Despite the cold they were stark naked. Their faces were hideous with paint; their skin coated with grease. Charles knew that they were cannibals. He had been told that in winter when food was scarce, they killed their old women. They had dogs, but they never killed them. Dogs were useful in hunting, old women were not.

The fauna of Tierra del Fuego was as strange as its people. The country was about the size of Scotland. It had quite a variety of plants. Why then, wondered Charles Darwin, were there so few beetles? Why so few butterflies and bees, and no crickets at all? He had come upon some kind of sea slug and found no more than seven of them, though for weeks he had searched under every stone. At the same time he had estimated over two hundred thousand eggs in the area. Of this number how few developed! Charles Lyell had referred to "the struggle for existence." Charles Darwin seemed to see the struggle take place.

On the lake a steamer duck floated past. It used its wings as paddles and had a powerful beak which it used to break open and feed on shellfish. Do species change in order to win out in the struggle for existence? Charles remembered seeing in the Falkland Islands an animal with gleaming eyes, half fox, half wolf. If it were fox, it was the largest he had ever seen; if wolf, why the foxlike legs?

The clanging of a bell rang through the air. It was the *Beagle* calling its naturalist aboard. As he climbed down to the shore it seemed to him that he had begun to sense a glimmer of light through the muddle.

III

16 Hart Street, Bloomsbury
December 26, 1836

To Charles Darwin, Esq.
My dear Sir:
I have read your paper with the greatest pleasure. Will you come up on January 2, and dine with us at half-past five o'clock, or come at five and I will go over the paper before dinner.
Yours very truly,
Charles Lyell

So began a lifelong friendship. At first it was based entirely on a shared interest in geology. From his five years of voyaging on the *Beagle* Darwin had brought back a great deal of new information on changes the earth was undergoing. He had discovered, for instance, that the western coast of South America was elevating more and more. He had studied the coral islands of the Pacific and was able to explain how they had risen from the sea. Geological changes are too slow for human perception. They have to be inferred, and Charles Darwin won the admiration of the older Charles by his brilliant reasoning.

A third person joined them. He was Joseph Hooker, who became England's foremost botanist. What talk went on! The trio ranged over the entire field of biology and their common interest knit them together with close bonds of affection.

There was one topic that Charles Darwin kept secret. He had become convinced that species were not immutable, that they change just as the earth changes. Like the earth, the change from one species of animal to another takes effect over such immense stretches of time that it can only be inferred from certain evidence. In Darwin's opinion the evidence was certain. But he still did not dare breathe a word of it to anyone, not even to his best friends. Even they might turn against him. As for the general public, their feelings would be outraged. No, before he spoke he had to have his proofs so well in hand that they would be incontrovertible. It might take years, but until then he had to keep silent.

Then one day he let the cat out of the bag. Charles Lyell was saying that in the deepest strata of rocks there were no mammals to be found and that only gradually in the overlying strata appeared warm-blooded quadrupeds.

"Can you explain the change in fauna?" asked

Charles Darwin. "I mean why or how one species sup-plants another?"

"Well, take the giant lizards, now. Along came the ice age. The world froze. Vegetation died and so did the vegetarian lizards. The stage was set for another species to make its debut."

"And where did the later species come from?"

"Ah, who can solve that mystery?"

"Who indeed! By the way, have you read Thomas Malthus?"

"Yes. He believes there are always more stomachs than food for them."

"Which leads to what you yourself call the 'struggle for existence.' In the jungles of South America I watched the struggle go on before my eyes."

"The struggle is real enough," said Charles Lyell. "How does that fact help us with the question of the origin of the species?"

Darwin did not answer at once. He seemed to be making up his mind. "In this struggle," he said at last, "wouldn't you say that those who win out are in some way better equipped than the losers?"

"Of course."

"And the weaker die out. Nature seems to act like our horse-breeders or pigeon-fanciers. She selects the qualities that suit best."

Charles Lyell knit his brows in doubt. "Well, per-haps. But since that does not affect the species it-self . . ."

Darwin plunged ahead. "But doesn't it? If natural selection goes far enough, goes on and on, producing creatures more and better adapted to their environment, then wouldn't it in time affect the form of the species? Wouldn't it change the species?"

"You mean to say you believe that species are not fixed?"

"Just that. Are you shocked?"

Lyell gave him a smile. "I, no. But many people will be when you publish your remarkable theory."

"I'm afraid so. Anyway, I'm not ready to tell them for a while yet. When I do, it will be difficult to refute my argument, I believe."

"You may even convince me," laughed Lyell. "Though right now your theory seems very farfetched. Anyway, the general public won't be shocked because they aren't interested in what doesn't concern them directly, and you do leave mankind out of your notion of natural selection."

Charles Darwin was silent.

"Surely you don't include man in this . . . this evolution of the species?"

"Is man outside nature? I see no evidence that he is exempt from the operation of natural law."

"There is a divine law."

"Yes, but we scientists can deal only with what happens in nature."

"True enough. But your theory appalls me just the same. It means that all living species may have arisen from a common ancestor in the primordial slime. Do you know, my dear Darwin, I believe I am going to be shocked after all. But all the same I shall try to keep an open mind."

The trio of friends did not mention the theory out-

side their private circle. But year after year they kept
after Darwin to announce it.

"There will be an outcry, of course," said Joseph
Hooker. "You will make enemies. But in the struggle
for survival you and your theory may win out."

Year after year Darwin put off publishing his work,
saying to his two friends, "Not yet. I am not quite
ready."

As they examined the data Hooker and Lyell became
convinced that Darwin's theory was right and that he
was indeed ready. "Hurry," they warned. "If you don't
publish your work soon someone will get in ahead of
you and rob you of the credit."

Someone did get in. One day a manuscript arrived
for Charles Darwin. It was written by a young naturalist, a Mr. Alfred Wallace, who just then was collecting
specimens in the Moluccas. The manuscript was a
statement of the theory of natural selection exactly as
Darwin himself conceived it. A polite note accompanied the manuscript requesting Darwin's opinion of it.
If Mr. Darwin thought well of it would he kindly pass
it on to Sir Charles Lyell, and perhaps arrange for its
publication.

Darwin was crushed. "You were right," he said
mournfully. "This young man has got in ahead of me.
The credit now belongs to him."

"No," expostulated Joseph Hooker. "We will not
permit it. You have been working on the theory for
twenty years. We cannot permit you to throw away
your just claim to the discovery."

Darwin shook his head. "The young man trusted me.
It is a matter of my honor. Having been silent so long I

shall have to remain silent. I intend to arrange for the publication of Mr. Wallace's paper."

"Let us write to Mr. Wallace and tell him the whole story as Hooker and I know it," suggested Sir Charles.

Reluctantly Darwin consented.

Alfred Wallace's reply overwhelmed the trio by its modesty and its magnanimity. Of course, he wrote, the credit belonged to Mr. Darwin alone.

It was Darwin's turn to be magnanimous. He insisted that Wallace's and his own statement should be published jointly. And so it was.

Charles Lyell was eventually won over to his friend's theory of the origin of species. So was every other biologist. Many, however, agree with Lyell that mankind is exceptional in one crucial respect. Like all creatures man is of course part of nature and subject to natural law. But, as Lyell believed, there is a part of man outside the realm of nature; for instance, the conscience of a Charles Darwin and the generosity of an Alfred Wallace.

Gregor Johann Mendel

(1822–1884)

THE MODEST MONK

I

A MAN sat in the library turning the pages of a dusty journal of science. He was not simply passing the time. He was a professor of botany searching for light on urgent questions that had arisen in the minds of all botanists. Suddenly the professor started, arrested by a title in faded print on a yellowing page. As he read on he could hardly contain himself. Unless he was mistaken, here was the answer to those urgent questions. The professor was not mistaken.

The account he was reading described an experiment begun forty-three years before and completed after eight long years. Why all this time had it been gathering dust? The author was a certain Gregor Mendel. Who in the name of truth was he? Why had not a monument been erected to his memory?

In the same year, 1900, two other scientists in other lands independently sought the same article. Thus, three scientists, each working on what he thought to be his own discovery of the laws of heredity, discovered Mendel.

As a boy Johann Mendel lived and worked on his father's farm outside a village in the foothills of the Moravian mountains, in the old Austro-Hungarian Empire.

The teacher in the village school was interested in fruit growing and beekeeping. He, therefore, added these subjects to the lessons of his pupils, and used the school garden in order to teach them his hobbies. He recognized Johann's exceptional talents. Although the Mendel family was poor, the teacher urged Johann's parents to send him away for further schooling. Only by pinching and sacrifice did the family finally manage it. Johann studied Latin and mathematics in high school, but his chief interest was in science, mainly botany.

To study further, he entered the monastery in Brünn. Brother Gregor, as he was now known, was a stocky man of medium height. He had blue eyes and curly brown hair over a high forehead. The abbot of the monastery permitted him to teach school. Because of his cheerful nature, his kindliness and enthusiasm for the subject he taught, his pupils one and all were devoted to him.

II

There was a bit of a mystery about Brother Gregor. He raised bees and bred mice. Such hobbies were understandable. But why he grew peas was not understandable, for he did not grow them as food. The monastery was enclosed by white walls. Next to one of the walls, in a strip of garden a hundred and twenty feet

long and a little over twenty feet wide, cut off by a
hedge, was Brother Gregor's private garden. There, on
fine spring days he could be found among his plants,
which he supported with staves and strings. He grew
hundreds of pea plants; some with white, others with
purple flowers; some tall, others drawf. Everybody in
the monastery relished fresh peas but Brother Gregor
did not grow them to be eaten. It was plain that he had
another purpose in mind.

If you watched him you saw him gently open with
forceps a still-unopened blossom. He removed the keel
and detached the anthers. Turning to another plant, he
dusted the pollen of the first upon the stigma of the second. Then he wrapped the plant in a bag of calico.
This he did to prevent bees from visiting the plant and
depositing upon it pollen from other plants. The mystery was why he was doing it.

"No mystery at all," said some of the monks. "It is
Brother Gregor's way of worshiping God. In one part
of his garden he takes care of bees, in another he makes
nests for mice. You may see him taking note of the
winds of heaven to try to determine their effect on our
weather. He tries to understand God's universe and all
his creatures. Even the humble pea."

"You resemble your father," Johann Mendel had
been told.

"Why do some people resemble their father, other
people their mother?" wondered Brother Gregor. A
child might resemble his father in height, his mother in
color of eyes. "One of our monks is red-haired. Neither
his father nor his mother is red-haired. But his grandfa-

ther is. How does heredity operate? How does nature regulate it?"

It was a strange question to put to a pea. However, Gregor Mendel knew that the answer to a scientific question was to be found by experiment only, and the pea plant was most apt for the experiment he had in mind. If he put the question properly the garden pea would give the right answer. This was how Gregor Mendel put the question: "What will be the offspring of mating a tall with a short plant, or of a purple with a white plant?"

The question did not concern garden peas only. It concerned all living things born of seed. It concerned mankind.

He knew that left to themselves tall plants produce seeds which bring forth tall plants. Similarly, short plants produce short plants. Suppose, however, he crossed a tall with a short?

He did. He took pollen from the flower of a short plant, not more than two feet high, and scattered it in the flower of one six feet high. The result was interesting: every one of the offspring of the marriage was tall. "Tallness," he recorded in his notebook, "dominates over shortness. Tallness is a dominant trait."

Now for the second generation: he waited for the tall children to form ripe seeds, and sowed them. You might call the new plants the grandchildren of the first marriage of tall with short. What happened now was remarkable: of the grandchildren one out of every four was short. Precisely one out of every four was short and three tall. "Shortness," recorded Mendel, "is a recessive trait."

He suspected that the inheritance of human traits might follow the same rule. But he refrained from jumping to conclusions. He continued his experiment with peas. When he sowed the seeds of the third generation, the three-to-one group, a new rule was discovered: the short plant gave out only short offspring; one of the three tall ones gave out only talls. But the remaining two tall ones gave offspring in the ratio now familiar to Mendel: three talls to one short.

He sowed more generations of the tall-short pea plants, always with the same results: of every group of four offspring three had the dominant trait of tallness and one the recessive shortness. The short bred shorts, one of the talls talls only, and the remaining two talls a mixture of three talls to one short.

Now the question was: did all inherited traits follow the dominant-recessive rule? Size did. What of other traits?

At the same time that he bred pea plants for size, in another corner of his garden he was breeding them for different traits. He had crossed a smooth with a wrinkled variety; green pods with yellow pods; one whose flowers grew on the axis with a kind whose flowers were bunched at the top. In all, he was investigating seven different traits. Never before had it occurred to anyone to do this.

In every case the result was the same as with size. Descendants of the original pair inherited the trait according to the dominant-recessive rule.

For eight years Gregor Mendel bred generations of garden peas. When he was sure of his results he thought, "Now I shall share my discovery with my colleagues in the Scientific Society. How delighted they will be."

So one icy evening in the winter of 1865, carrying his papers, he trudged for several miles on a country road to the meeting of the Scientific Society held at the high school at Brünn. Some forty members attended, most of them professors of science. Besides Mendel there was a speaker on the topic of Charles Darwin's book *Origin of the Species*. This came first on the program.

As the speaker explained Darwin's theories, new at the time, the audience grew excited. Darwin argued that in nature there are more stomachs than food to fill them. In the course of the struggle to keep alive, that kind of creature wins out which has some physical advantage over its competitor. The weaker is eliminated. The winner perpetuates his kind — until one stronger makes his appearance. That, according to Darwin, is how nature selects and decrees which kind of animal or plant shall survive, which disappear.

The professors' familiar world of biology began to topple.

Gregor Mendel took the floor amid buzz and echoes. ("Struggle for existence . . . survival of the fittest . . .") Amid such sonorous phrases he began to talk about the simple garden pea. In a quiet voice he read off some statistics. "One out of four. Tall and dwarf. Purple and white. Three out of four dominant." In one hour he summarized the results of eight years of careful work. But the audience was still dazed from the shock of Darwin upon their ingrained beliefs. Gregor Mendel sat down. No discussion followed, not a single question was asked of him. The meeting adjourned. Outside on the icy road the professors resumed their expostulation over Darwin.

"It's clear," they agreed, "why the seal, say, needs fur and the tiger his great strength. Without such equipment they wouldn't survive. But how does it happen that they come by their equipment in the first place? What in their bodily nature brings it out?"

Had they listened to Brother Gregor they would have heard the answer, the mechanics for natural selection. They had paid no attention to him or his arithmetic with garden peas. They could not imagine that the paper they had listened to without ears would some day form the basis of a new branch of biology called genetics. They had no way of knowing that a later generation would erect at Brünn a monumental statue to the man they had ignored.

Brother Gregor went quietly back to his cell in the monastery. He was not in the least put out by the misfire of his paper. "My time will surely come," he said confidently.

III

The rediscovery of Mendel's article and the confirmation of his theory by the three botanists in 1900 attracted the attention of the world. Mendel's writing was now understood, and within a year it was being taught in universities.

Physicians found that certain inherited diseases of man followed Mendel's law — for instance, hemophilia. People with hemophilia are "bleeders," suffering from an inherited tendency to uncontrollable bleeding. Blue and brown eyes, red and blond hair, red-green color blindness — these and every other inherited trait obeyed the law Mendel had discovered.

Scientists began to devise many experiments to study the inherited characteristics of animals and plants.

Probably the most striking application of Mendel's theory was the development of hybrid corn. The origin of maize is lost in history. All we know is that the American Indians had developed the plant over thousands of years. The Europeans who explored the New World brought the maize plant to Europe.

By using the Mendelian theory, agricultural scientists undertook extensive experiments to improve its yield. They began by inbreeding certain types of maize in order to get particular strains which had desirable characteristics. Then, following Mendel, the inbred lines were crossed. The result in the courses of generations was a vigorous hybrid offspring superior not only to the parents but also to the varieties of maize from which the inbred had been originally isolated.

By bringing together the factors from several varieties, crossbreeding produced new varieties which combined the desirable qualities of the parent stock.

The results have been spectacular. Hybrid corn, which is derived from many strains, is bred today for its high yields per acre. Other characteristics that have been developed are earlier maturity and resistance to disease and drought. Hybrid corn constitutes at present almost the entire corn crop of the United States.

Among other benefits to mankind, Gregor Mendel showed the way to provide sufficient food for mankind.

INDEX

INDEX